Science 4

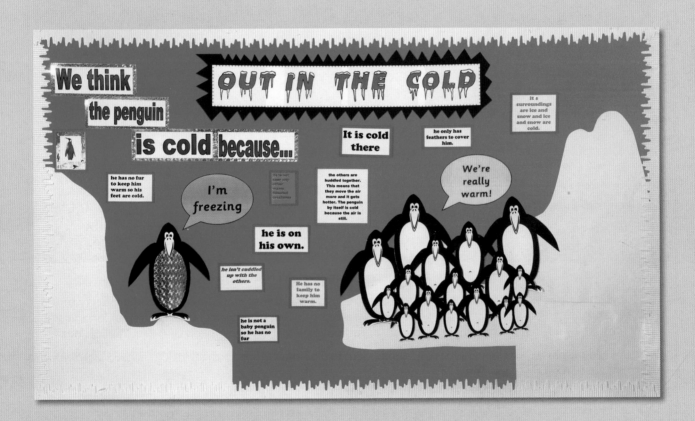

Carolyn Dale

Acknowledgements

To everyone in these Maidenhead primary schools who worked so hard to meet deadlines and to produce work of such a high quality for this book, a big, big thank you: Lowbrook School, Knowl Hill; St Edmund Campion RC School; Claires Court Schools, The Ridgeway, Waltham St Lawrence; White Waltham C of E School and Woodlands Park School, and to Juniper Hill Primary School, Flackwell Heath, Marlow.

Without them there would be no book at all!

A very special big thank you goes to Mary Gallop and Jean Davies of Lowbrook School who enthusiastically produced so much work for the book and lent their children to try out some of the activities; to Shirley Craddock, a talented and creative ex-colleague, who worked tirelessly in putting finishing touches to displays; and to Zoë Parish, Paul Naish and Steve Forest for their patience and advice.

And last, but by no means least, my family and friends who have had to live with these books for a long time: I do hope that everyone – friends, family and colleagues – appreciate the final result!

From Habitats on page 24

Commissioning Editor: Zoë Parish   Editor: Janet Swarbrick   Cover Design: Sophie Pelham
Page Layout: Barbara Linton   Photography: Steve Forest   Illustrations: Ruth Murray

First published in 2008 by Belair Publications.

ISBN 978-1-84191-464-0

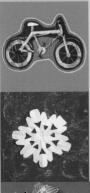

Contents

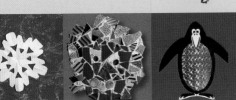

Moving and Growing

These grids demonstrate the learning objectives covered in the activities within the theme. The curriculum references indicate the relevant programme of study (PoS) for a subject area unless otherwise stated.

	Learning Objectives	Curriculum References
Science (Page 6)		
Scientific Enquiry	Consider how to answer a question about movement.	Sc1/2b
	Pose questions that can be investigated scientifically.	Sc1/2a
Life Processes and Living Things (QCA Science Unit 4A)	Name the structure and some of the bones in the human skeleton.	Sc2/2e
	Describe the functions of a skeleton.	Sc2/2e
	Explain how bones and muscles help us move.	Sc2/2e
	Describe the skeletons of other animals and relate to how they move.	Sc2/2e
Physical Processes	Identify the forces of push or pull and their opposing forces.	Sc4/2e
Literacy (Page 8)		
Creating and Shaping Texts	Devise movement poems.	En3/1a-e;2a-e;12
	Compose stories about growth.	En3/1a-e;2a-e;12
	Present similar information in different ways to suit a given reader.	En3/1b-d
	Research and write fiction and non-fiction texts about bones.	En1/3a-e; En3/1a-e;2a-e;12
Understanding and Interpreting Texts	Find out about the skeletons of humans and other animals.	En2/3a-c
Group Discussion and Interaction	Present stories about bones to others as part of a group.	En1/1a-f; ICT PoS 1a-c;2a,b
	Organise a presentation suitable for younger children.	ICT PoS 1a-c;2a,b
Mathematics (Page 10)		
Understanding Shape	Make symmetrical shapes.	Ma3/2b-c
	Copy shapes onto a grid.	Ma3/2c;3c
	Recognise and name different quadrilaterals and triangles.	Ma3/2b
	Draw rectangles and triangles and calculate perimeters. Calculate areas in squares.	Ma3/2b;4e
Measuring	Make linear measurements of parts of our bodies.	Ma3/1a;4a
	Name the eight points of the compass and know that angles are measured in degrees.	Ma3/2a
Handling Data	Make a database of measurements of children in the class.	Ma4/2c; ICT PoS 1a-c
	Draw and interpret bar graphs of different measurements of our bodies.	Ma4/2b,c,f

Moving and Growing

Learning Objectives	Curriculum References
Design & Technology (Page 12)	
Make models of bones to show structure.	PoS 2a-e;3a-c
Make skeleton puppets.	PoS 1a-d;2a-e;3a-c;4a,b;5a-c
Make moving figures from a variety of materials using different techniques.	PoS 1a-d;2a-f;3a-c;4a,b;5a-c; QCA Design and Technology Unit 4B
Make pirates' treasure chests and fill them with treasure.	PoS 1a-d;2a-f;3a-c;4a,b;5a-c; QCA Design and Technology Unit 4A
Geography (Page 12)	
Trace the journey of an explorer or nation of explorers of the past or present.	PoS 2a-d
Draw an imaginary map on a grid. Use grid references and compass directions to describe a journey to find treasure.	PoS 2a-c; QCA Geography Unit 25; ITC PoS 2b
Control and compare a floor turtle and a computer screen turtle.	PoS 2a-c; QCA Geography Unit 25; ITC PoS 2a-c; QCA ICT Unit 4E
PSHCE (Page 12)	
Find out about the importance of diet and exercise in making strong muscles and bones.	PoS 3a; QCA Citizenship Unit 02
Look at bone X-rays and find out how broken bones heal, and how doctors and nurses help us.	PoS1e;3a;5e
Art (Page 14)	
Using an imaginary or real bone as a stimulus draw or construct imaginary animals.	PoS 1a-c;2a-c;3a,b;4a,b;5a-c
Express movement in pictures.	PoS1a-c;4c
Use a variety of materials and processes to communicate ideas about movement and growth, and make and design images and artefacts.	PoS1a;4c
History (Page 14)	
Find out about the movements and conquests of an ancient civilisation such as the Romans, Vikings or Anglo Saxons. Make a case study.	PoS 1a;2a-d;4a,b; QCA History Unit 6A;6B;6C;10
Find out about Tudor ships that have been discovered and how they tell about the life of people of those times.	PoS 1a;2a-d;4a,b;5a-c; QCA History Unit 8
Music (Page 14)	
Devise an accompaniment to a skeleton dance.	PoS 1b-c;2a,b
Devise a story with musical accompaniment about two skeletons.	PoS 1b-c;2a,b
Listen to *Danse macabre* by Saint-Saëns.	PoS 4a
PE (Page 14)	
Move like skeletons to music.	PoS 6a,b
Make a series of symmetrical movements with a partner.	PoS 6a,b; QCA PE Unit 15

Moving and Growing

Starting Points

- Look at a model of a human skeleton and talk about the different bones.

- Examine a bone. List as many descriptive words as possible about its properties, such as 'hard', 'white', 'spongy in the middle'. Explain why bones have each

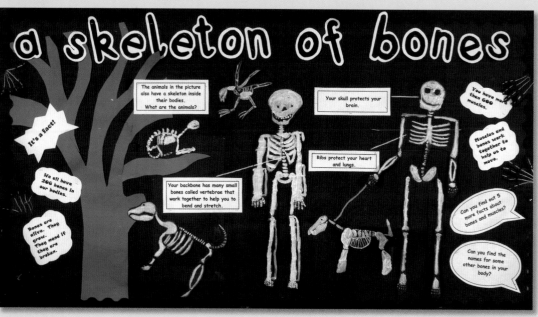

of the properties, for example 'They are hollow so are not very heavy, enabling us to move about easily'; 'They are hard as they need to be strong', and so on.

- Talk about the three functions of a skeleton: support, movement and protection.

Support: the children should try to move as if they had no skeleton at all. They will be floppy and on the ground.

Movement: the children should move as if their skeleton has no joints in it, keeping arms, legs, fingers and so on stiff. Discuss joints as places where bones meet.

Protection: the children should oint to the bones around the brain, spine and heart and explain why they think the bones are there.

Enquiry

- Draw around the body shape of a child lying flat on black sugar paper or newspaper, and cut it out. Draw the main bones in the arms, legs and body onto the shape in white paint or chalk. Label some bones such as 'ribs', 'skull', 'backbone' and say what they do. For example: the skull protects the brain; the ribs protect the heart and lungs; the leg bones support the body and help it to move.

- Sort bones in the body into three lists of those that are used mainly for movement, mainly for protection and mainly for support.

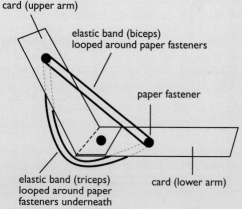

Extension Activities

- Make a cardboard arm (see the diagram) to show how bones and muscles work together to help movement. When the lower arm is held down, the biceps muscle is relaxed and stretched and the triceps muscle contracts. When the lower arm is raised, the biceps contracts and the triceps relaxes and gets stretched.

- Use the activity sheet on page 7. Compare skeletons of familiar animals with that of a human and match parts that are similar in two or more skeletons. Identify which animal each skeleton comes from.

- Make a skeleton display. Use paint for the main bones as chalk is too easily smudged.

- Discuss animals that do not have a skeleton inside them but on the outside of their bodies, such as insects. Introduce and explain the terms 'endoskeleton' and 'exoskeleton'.

Whose skeleton?

These are the skeletons of a bird, a dog, a fish and a human. Can you label them with the correct name?

Look at the skeletons of the bird and the human.

Can you think of five ways they are the same and five ways they are different?

Comparing a bird and a human skeleton

Similarities	Differences

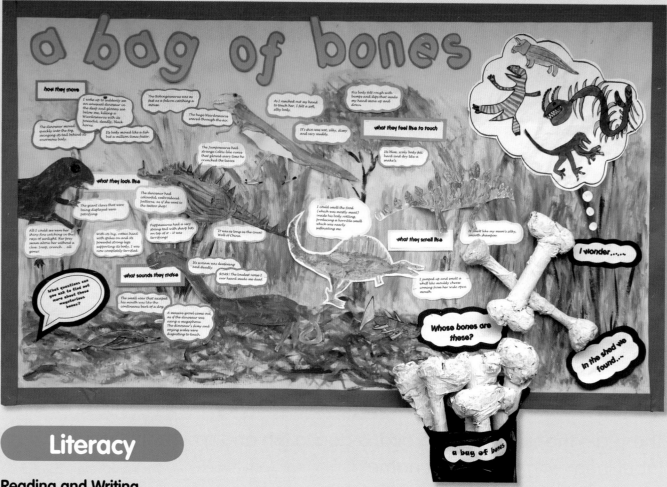

Literacy

Reading and Writing

- Make up models of bones using paper and tubes or other ways suggested by the children. Put the bones in a bag (see display above) and use it as a starting point for creative writing (see activity sheet on page 9).

- Paint or draw a small sketch of the type of animal that one of the bones might have come from. Decide on one aspect of the animal, for example how it moves, and write three sentences to describe it.

- Devise lists of words that describe the movement of the animal. Use the words to create a poem.

- Compose stories on a theme of growth, using the story of 'Jack and the beanstalk' as an example. Present ideas about what would grow out of the bean and write descriptions of subsequent adventures.

- Make a factual booklet in a bone shape about bones and skeletons of humans and/or other animals.

- Devise similes and metaphors about bones, such as 'as white as shivering bones', 'like sticks of white rock jumping about' or 'moving shapes of white tissue paper' and so on.

Speaking and Listening

- Present information and stories about bones and skeletons to younger children. Research the audience first to find out what they know and their interests. Focus on animals or humans and use a variety of methods to relate the information, such as drama or audience participation in songs and poems and so on.

Moving and Growing

A bag of bones

Here is a paragraph for the beginning of a story.

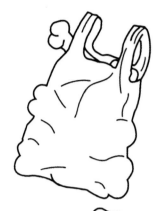

Imagine John's amazement when he and Bobs the dog walked into the old potting shed one day in the school holidays. There in the corner, covered with cobwebs, was a very odd-shaped bag with what looked like old bones sticking out of it. Very cautiously John peeped into the bag.

What happens next? Make up a paragraph to describe what John and Bobs see.

Will you make the readers happy, excited or scared? Will you make them laugh?

_____

_____

_____

_____

_____

_____

_____

_____

_____

_____

 **Finish your story on a separate page.**
REMEMBER to choose words and phrases carefully.

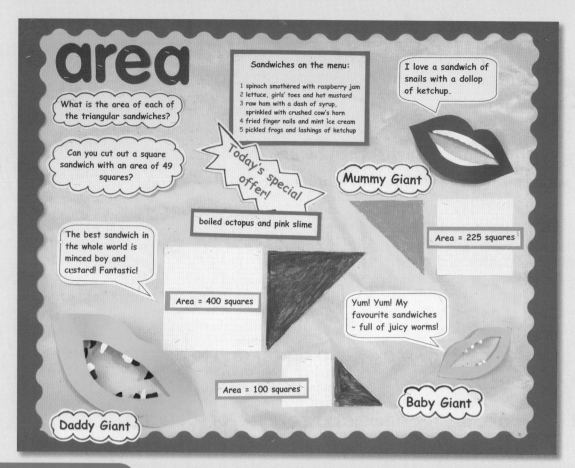

Maths

Understanding Shape

- Explore how shapes can 'grow' and 'shrink': cut slices of bread in half in different ways, then into quarters. Ask the children to name each shape then estimate and measure the shapes' sizes at each stage. Use the measurements to draw each shape on squared paper. Match the drawn shapes to the real pieces of bread to see how accurate the measurements are.

- Make up a grid and draw a square, triangle or rectangle on it. Calculate perimeters and areas of simple shapes. Make each shape bigger or smaller, by halving or doubling the areas, to create sandwiches for a giant family as shown on the display above. Make up imaginary giant sandwiches with tasty fillings – for giants!

- Explore and name the eight points of the compass. The children need to know about measurement in degrees and that there are 360 degrees in a complete turn. Make up an imaginary map on a grid on which there is some hidden treasure. Provide written directions, including compass references, to a treasure (see the activity sheet on page 11). Children use the compass references to find the treasure. Completing the grid references to find the treasure links to Geography (see page 12).

- Draw symmetrical shapes of faces and bodies on grids. Challenge children to copy them into another quadrant.

Measuring

- Pose some measuring questions about movement, such as 'Can the person with the longest arms throw a ball the furthest?' 'Does the person with the longest legs run the fastest?' Gather some ideas from the children.

Handling Data

- Ask the children to measure the height of each other. Present the heights on a table and then transfer them onto a graph or scattergram using the computer.

- Make up a database about children in the class that includes numerical facts. They should choose and name the fields. Ask the children questions about the data. Groups could use the database to make up a display about some aspect of the class, for example one group could order heights, one could order jumping heights and another the lengths of feet and hands.

Find the treasure

Draw the route to the treasure on this map.

Write the grid references in the brackets as for Sandy Beach.

Start at Sandy Beach (B1) and travel east to Blue River Rocks (   ).
By boat, travel north to Pirate's Creek (   ), then north-east to Echo
Caves (   ). Walk north to Jelly Jones' House (   ), then south-east
to the Signpost (   ). Walk north-east to Peter's Cove (   ) then
north-west to the base of the Old Windmill (   ). Turn south to Miller's
Grave (   ) and north-west to Donkey Bridge (   ). Climb north-
west to Needle Mountain (   ). Travel west to the Palm Tree Huts
(   ), then south to Flamingo Lake Waterfall (   ). Continue
south-west to the Grass Hut (   ) where the treasure is hidden.

**Decide on a new place to hide the treasure and write
instructions showing how to get there. Include compass
directions and grid references.**

Design & Technology

- Provide materials to make models of bones. Use card for outside and straws for the inside to show that bones are not solid.

- Using rolls of paper or straws for bones, make skeleton puppets that move. Feed string or thread through the tubes to allow movement at joints. Use the puppets to develop a story or play about pirates. Make the treasure chest with a lid that can be opened and closed (see the activity sheet on page 13). Look at containers and consider materials, shapes, sizes, linings and so on, Reproduce the design of the chest, perhaps producing a set of three, making one 'shrink' and the other 'grow' bigger. Make different treasure chests, using a variety of materials, including textiles.

- Ask the children to make models of figures doing all kinds of movements, such as in dancing, using Modroc, clay or papier mâché (see the display above).

Geography

- Show the children the route (using compass directions) of a long distance traveller or explorer of the past or present, such Christopher Colombus (1451–1506) or the route of the America's Cup race, on a globe and a flat map of the world.

- Use the compass points and write grid references as on the activity sheet on page 11.

- Control a programmable floor turtle and compare a computer screen turtle. Draw shapes using commands of direction. The children could write simple programs to repeat patterns.

- Draw an imaginary map on a grid with a scale.

PSHCE

- Discuss the importance of diet and exercise in making strong muscles and bones. Devise and paint or draw an advertisement for a new food that will make bones and teeth strong and healthy and an advertisement with a slogan about the importance of exercising such as dancing, skipping, walking and running.

- Look at bone X-rays. Investigate how broken bones are mended, and the roles of doctors and nurses.

Moving and Growing

My treasure chest

Trace this net for a cuboid treasure chest onto card. Cut it out and use the tabs to stick it together. Allow it to dry and decorate it.

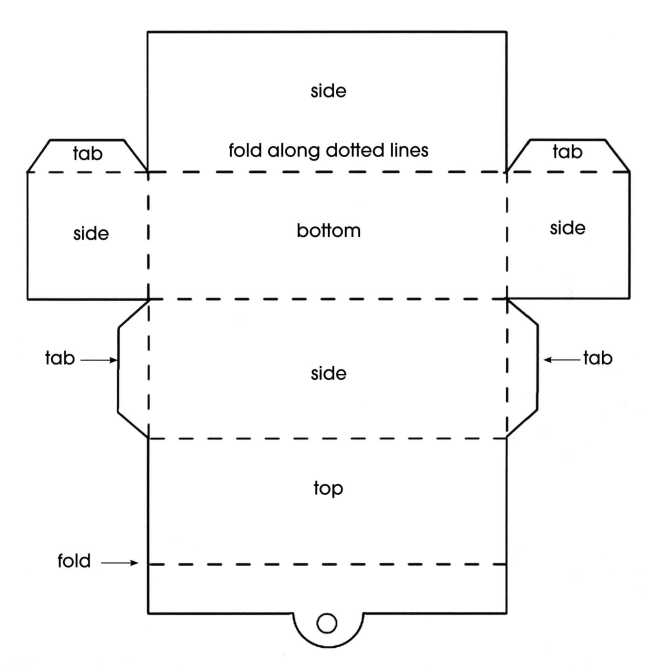

Can you make a chest of the same design but bigger or smaller?

Design a chest of your own and make it using various materials. How will you open and close the lid? What will be inside?

Art

- Use a real or model bone as a stimulus to draw, paint or construct imaginary animals from a variety of media.

- Look at pictures of cave paintings, Aboriginal art and so on and consider how movement is depicted. Children make up their own story in pictures of an event in the past such as the killing of an animal or an attack in a battle.

- Cut out a shape of a human or animal, then repeat it, changing the shape slightly for each position and paste the shapes in different positions to show movement. Repeat with other shapes or animals.

- Make faces 'grow'. First, plan a face using blocks of colour in coloured pencils on paper, then construct it in the following way: break up differently coloured glass and pottery items. It is safer for adults to do the breaking and select safe pieces for the children to use. Arrange the pieces into a face with a glue-gun onto a board. Put tile cement between each piece and wipe off the excess before it dries.

History

- Study journeys and ways of life of the Anglo-Saxons, the Romans or the Vikings. Study specific artefacts and what we learn from them. Children could place special events on a time-line alongside their own families to show how long ago it was.

- Find out about ships and the activity of Tudor pirates on the seas during this period. What was life like at sea at this time? How was it different for officers (rich) and crew (poor). Develop this into discussions and written comparisons of rich and poor of the time.

Music

- Devise a short story about two skeletons, choosing appropriate instruments and sounds, as on activity sheet on page 15.

- Look at model skeletons. Make them dance and devise an accompaniment to describe their movements. Link this with music when listening to *Danse macabre* by Saint-Saëns (1835–1921).

PE

- Move like skeletons to music, such as *Danse macabre* by Saint-Saëns. Encourage a light-hearted approach to this, not a 'macabre' one.

- Devise a dance sequence of symmetrical movements with a partner to tell a story. Mime movements and hold a feedback session so spectators can relate what they think is happening.

- Take photos of the children in active poses. Magnify them on a photocopier. The children stick straws on the bodies to show the main bones and the different position of them in each movement.

Moving and Growing

Bones talking

What do you think the skeletons are saying to each other? Write it in the speech bubbles.

NOW!

Work with a partner and make up a short presentation to tell the story of the two skeletons. Add musical instruments as an accompaniment. Choose your percussion instruments carefully.

Habitats

These grids demonstrate the learning objectives covered in the activities within the theme. The curriculum references indicate the relevant programme of study (PoS) for a subject area unless otherwise stated.

	Learning Objectives	Curriculum References
Science (Page 18)		
Scientific Enquiry	Look at patterns of behaviour of living things and communities and think about their causes.	Sc1/1a
	Ask closed questions to sort a collection of living things.	Sc1/2a; ICT PoS 5a; QCA ICT Unit 4C
	Compare living things.	Sc1/2e-m
Life Processes and Living Things (QCA Science Unit 4B)	Recognise different habitats, conditions and living things there.	Sc2/5b
	Make and interpret keys to sort animals and plants.	Sc2/4a; ICT PoS 5b
	Represent habitats that named animals require.	Sc2/5b
Literacy (Page 20)		
Group Discussion and Interaction	When working in a group present information about a habitat.	En1/1a-f
Listening and Responding	Participate in a role play of a court case of a predator.	En1a-f;4a-c
Creating and Shaping Texts	Write fantastic facts about animals studied.	En3/1a,b
	Compose poems and short descriptive verses about found animals. Imagine them looking our of their habitat 'windows'.	En3/2a-f
	Devise posters and take photographs to show how to care for the environment.	En3/1a-e; ICT PoS 1a,b;3a,b;4a-c
Understanding and Interpreting Texts	Read information and find out about selected animals, plants and habitats.	En2/3a-e; ICT PoS 1a,b;3a,b;5a,b
Mathematics (Page 22)		
Knowing and Using Number Facts/Calculating	Use animal patterns to find patterns in number.	Ma2/2a;3f
	Learn about digital roots.	Ma2/2a;3f
Measuring	Measure size of animals and plants and make comparisons.	Ma3/1a;4a
Handling Data	Represent animal and plant data on a table and as graphs.	Ma4/1a-e;2b,d,f
	Complete a tally chart and interpret it.	Ma4/1c,d;2c,f
	Use the computer to present graphs.	Ma4/2c; ICT PoS1b
Understanding Shape	Make and draw 2-D and 3-D shapes and patterns.	Ma3/1h;2b-d
	Visualise 3-D shapes from 2-D drawings.	Ma3/1h;2b-d

Learning Objectives	Curriculum References
Design & Technology (Page 24)	
Represent a habitat in a collage using a variety of materials.	PoS 1b-d;2a-f;3a
Construct accurate models of animals found using a variety of materials.	PoS 1b-d;2a-f;3a
Construct models of animals with moving parts.	PoS 1b-d;2a-f;3a
Art (Page 24)	
Use different materials to make displays to represent habitats of animals and plants. Paint animals camouflaged against the background.	PoS 1a-c;2a-c
PSHCE (Page 24)	
Discuss why and how wildlife should be protected, and how camouflage helps to protect many creatures..	PoS 5a,e
Use Aesop's fables to discuss behaviour and lifestyles.	PoS 1a-f
Geography (Page 26)	
Compare animals and plants found in different worldwide habitats.	PoS 3a,b; QCA Geography Unit 10
Identify habitats seen from the window in different places.	PoS 3a-e; QCA Geography Unit 10,21
Consider how habitats change and think about our responsibilities for the future.	PoS 3a-e; QCA Geography Unit 21
History (Page 26)	
Find out how habitats in the local area have changed and the effect on plants and animals.	PoS 7a; QCA History Unit 18
Find out about the lives of the ancient Egyptians and how animals were important as food or to be worshipped.	PoS 2a,b;4a,b; QCA History Unit 10
PE (Page 26)	
Move in ways of different animals and combine with others to make multi-legged animals.	PoS 6b;8a,b; QCA PE Unit 9
Name a habitat and make up the movements for an imaginary animal that lives there.	PoS 6b;8a,b; QCA PE Unit 9
Music (Page 26)	
Listen to music about animals and discuss how the composer creates effects.	PoS 4a,b
Devise own music to illustrate a certain animal.	PoS 2a,b; QCA Music Unit 11

Habitats

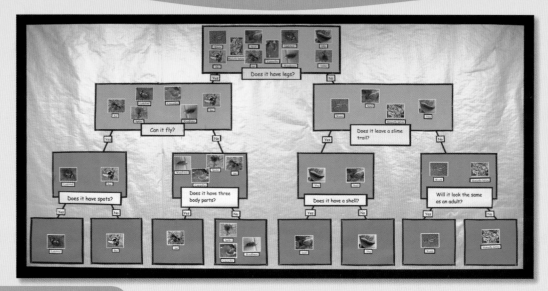

Science

Starting Points

- Find out children's ideas of what is an animal and what is a plant. They may not consider that an earthworm is an animal or a tree a plant. Ask groups to list all the animals and plants they observe in the school grounds.

- On a rough map of the school and its grounds mark different large habitats (places with certain conditions suited to the living things there) such as a field, the playground, bare ground, flower beds, a hedge, a pond and so on. Outside with the children, identify these and split a selected large habitat into mini-habitats such as under stones, in the grass, on bare earth and so on. Identify conditions in each habitat.

Enquiry

- Name some minibeasts found locally and find out the conditions they need to survive. Give children time to research some facts about their animal, for example what food they eat, if they need water to drink, their preferred conditions, where they live. The children could design an animal passport first, giving this information on the activity sheet on page 19.

- Play the habitat game. Each child is a named minibeast. Hide the following around the classroom: green 'food' cards with a named plant or animal written on them; blue 'water' cards; red 'shelter' cards with 'plant', 'tree', 'rock', 'stone', 'soil', 'grass', 'water', and so on written on them; and brown 'condition' cards with 'dark', 'light', 'wet', 'dry', 'warm', 'cold' and so on written on them. Give the children a minute to find the cards that will keep them 'alive'. Repeat with different animals.

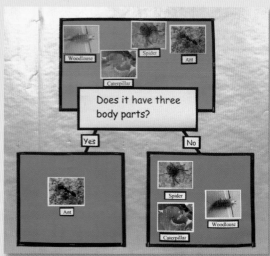

Extension Activities

- Help the children to devise keys such as a branching database for a group of minibeasts in their habitats (see display above). Select no more than six to eight minibeasts such as a snail, a slug, a butterfly, a bee, an earthworm, a woodlouse, an ant or a centipede. Remember that a key is sorted using observable features of the animal such as how many legs it has, whether it has a shell and so on. Follow each others' keys to see if they are accurate. Make up other keys about groups of plants or other animals.

- Identify the plants in a large habitat. Put a large hoop down in a field and count the different plants there. Do this randomly a few times. Collect a few samples of each plant, leaving plenty for animals' food, and carefully, without tearing the plant, include parts such as the root, stem, leaves and flowers.

Animal passport

For _____

Place photograph or drawing here.

Address _____

_____

_____

_____

Appearance

Colours _____

Number of legs _____

Size _____

Special features _____

Lifestyle

Way of moving _____

Conditions needed _____

Food _____

Habitats _____

_____

Literacy

Reading and Writing

- Write poems about one type of animal such as a spider and display them as a spider's web. The web could be painted or constructed of silver thread (see display above).

- Make up a 'fantastic facts' list about animals studied with the class, for example 'Did you know that ... for its size the ant has the biggest brain of all animals'; ' ... all insects have six legs'; ' ... there are 44 types of ladybird', and so on.

- Use the activity sheet on page 21 to write an address on an envelope for a particular animal that gives information about where it lives. Write an invitation to invite the animal to an event such as a swimming gala, a dance or a birthday party, remembering to give all the necessary information.

- Imagine an animal looking out of its habitat window and imagine what it sees, hears and feels. Together, devise short descriptive verses. Focus on using interesting verbs, adjectives or adverbs. Or write a group poem of five lines, one child to write a line for each sense (see display).

- Make posters and take photographs to advise people how to care for a habitat.

Speaking and Listening

- Select a carnivore, such as a spider, and write or act out a trial by a group of its prey (for example, flies accusing it of murder). Appoint a judge, prosecution and defence and a class jury. Present the case as in court.

- Ask the children to research information about an animal's habitat and to present it to others using a variety of ways, such as ICT, drawings and photographs.

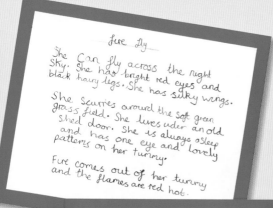

Habitats

Minibeasts' addresses

Miss Wendy Woodlouse
Under the Stone
Mary's Garden
Dark Village
Dampshire

Choose two other minibeasts. Write the address of each minibeast on the envelopes. Make sure the address tells something about where it lives (its habitat).

NOW!

Decide on a minibeast event and write an invitation to it on another sheet of paper.

Make sure you include details of where the event will be held (its habitat).

Maths

Using Number Facts

● Find out about the different types of ladybirds. The most common in Britain is the seven-spot. Use the number of spots on a ladybird to consolidate different number sequences and tables (see the display above).

● Learn about digital roots of numbers as follows.

1. Write the answers to a multiplication table such as the 9 × table.

2. Add the digits together for each answer until you get a single number. This is the digital root. For example, if the answer is 39, 3+9 = 12; then 1+2= 3, so the digital root is 3.

3. Look for the pattern in the digital roots. All tables have a pattern. (Children enjoy finding these patterns. For the 9 × table children will notice that all the digital roots are 9.)

Understanding Shape

● Look for mathematical shapes in a habitat, such as honeycomb hexagons, cylinders for stems and trunks of trees, and so on.

● Ask the children to use mathematical shapes to construct the bodies of animals and plants found.

Measuring

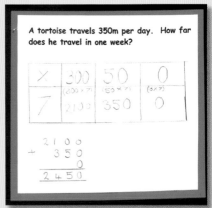

● Collect animals in mini-spectors with a grid on the bottom. Estimate the area of each. If possible measure several of the same species so children realise there is a variety in size. Discuss the possible reasons for variation, such as living conditions (where found), age and type. Sequence the different animals from smallest to largest. Use the collected data of frequency of animals to draw bar graphs. Encourage children to interrogate the data by forming questions about it.

Handling Data

● Keep a tally of the different animals in a given habitat over a period of time. Different groups could look at different large or small habitats or keep a whole class record.

● Sort a selection of the animals found in different ways such as in Venn diagrams, Carroll diagrams and keys. (See the activity sheet on page 23.) Note that a Carroll diagram always has one pair of alternatives: 'have' and 'have not'.

Habitats

A Carroll diagram

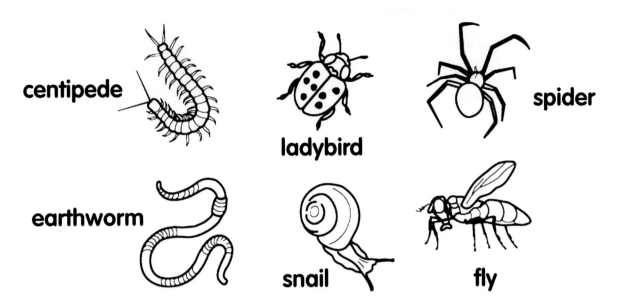

centipede

ladybird

spider

earthworm

snail

fly

Here are pictures of animals you may have found in and around grassland.

Look at them carefully and write their names in the correct place in the diagram below.

An animal (not pictured) has been written in each section for you already.

	Has 6 legs	Does not have 6 legs
Has wings	wasp	robin
Does not have wings	ant	woodlouse

What two things are similar about the animals in the striped section?

What two things are similar about the animals in the spotted section?

What other animals can you add to each section?

Can you find our camouflaged minibeasts?

A habitat is a place where plants and animals find what they need to survive.

We found these minibeasts in their own habitats in our wildlife area.

Design & Technology

- Represent a local habitat in a wall collage. Ensure children place animals in their correct location (see display above).

- Provide a variety of materials for the children to construct accurate models of animals found. The children should select materials for different body parts and join them in appropriate ways. They could find ways to make body parts of animals, such as legs, wings and antennae, move.

Art

- Look at animals that are camouflaged in their habitat and ask the children to make backgrounds and paint animals to hide them. Make a display of some animals that are well camouflaged, like cheetahs. Discuss why animals need to be camouflaged whether they are predators or prey.

PSHCE

- Read fables by Aesop (620–560 BCE), a Greek slave and storyteller, who lived in ancient Greece. Many are ideal as they are short stories full of description, each with a moral. Discuss the message in each. Encourage the children to act them out. List problems in school such as clearing up, bullying, litter and so on. Decide on a particular message and make up a fable using animals that the children have studied (see the activity sheet on page 25).

- Discuss how and why wildlife should be protected.

The fable of the ant and the frog

An ant <u>went out</u> one day down to the pond for a drink.

As he bent down, a frog <u>came out of</u> the water and <u>said</u>, 'Go away! This is our pond. We don't want you here!' The ant did not like it and <u>went</u> home.

The next day he <u>went again</u>. The same thing happened. He <u>went</u> home.

The third day ant took his friend with him. The frog's head <u>came out</u> of the water. But this time he didn't speak. He looked at ant's friend – a fat, black stag beetle with big claws – and <u>went</u> straight back down into the pond. He was frightened!

Write this fable again changing the underlined words for more interesting words or phrases.

NOW!

The moral of this story is that bullies don't win in the end. Make up a fable of your own with the title 'We Should Not be Greedy' or 'We Should Try to Live Together Happily'.

There are four rules.

1. The story must have a moral – a lesson in how to behave.
2. It should be short.
3. It must be interesting.
4. It should have animals in it that you have studied.

Geography

- Read *Window* by Jeannie Baker (Walker Books) and explore how habitats change over time. Relate the story to the children's own habitat. This and other books by the same author are aimed at making children think carefully about their own environment and their responsibilities (see the display above).

- Ask the children to look out of their window and draw what they see. Discuss their pictures and their likes and dislikes about it. See the activity sheet on page 27 and compare animals and plants found in different worldwide habitats.

- Provide a flat map and a globe for children to label different habitats, such as mountains, rivers, lakes, forests, deserts and so on and their features. Consider how and why each place is changing.

History

- Find out about the local area 50 to 100 years ago. List ways in which it has changed since then, discuss why and list ways in which it is better and worse now. Predict how it will be in the future and the effects on plants and animals.

- Find out how animals have been used by civilisations of the past. For example, animals were very important to the ancient Egyptians for food and as pets and some were worshipped. Many were mummified.

PE

- Study the movement of particular animals either at first hand or on film. Identify the ways the animals move and to try to copy them. For animals with more than four legs the children can work together to move in different ways.

- Name a habitat and make up the movements of an imaginary animal that lives there.

Music

- Listen to both classical and popular animal music such as the 'Flight of the bumblebee' from *Tsar Saltan* by Rimsky-Korsakov (1844–1908); *The Pink Panther* film theme music; 'We are Siamese' from Disney's film *The lady and the tramp*; and the *Carnival of the animals* by Saint-Saëns. Consider how well the composer tells us something about the animals.

- Create a recurring rhythm to illustrate the movement of an animal. Choose different sources of sound such as voices, bodies and instruments.

Looking through the window

Rachel lives in the United Kingdom.

Ravi lives in India.

When they look out of their windows, some things look the same. But one big difference is the kind of animals they might see.

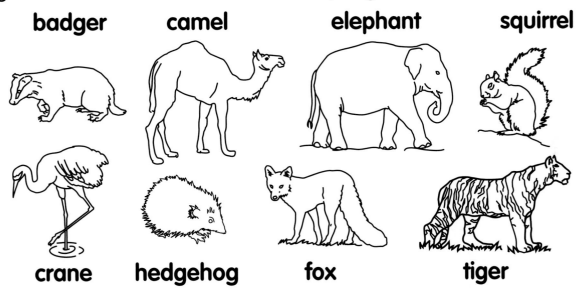

badger   **camel**   **elephant**   **squirrel**

crane   **hedgehog**   **fox**   **tiger**

Here are some of the animals they might see when they look out of their windows. Choose one of the children. Copy the window onto a big sheet of paper. Draw the animals that Rachel might see in the United Kingdom or that Ravi might see in India if they are lucky!

Think of more animals that each child might see and draw them too.

NOW! Choose another country and draw what a friend would see through the window there – it could be a desert or a very cold country.

Keeping Warm

These grids demonstrate the learning objectives covered in the activities within the theme. The curriculum references indicate the relevant programme of study (PoS) for a subject area unless otherwise stated.

	Learning Objectives	Curriculum References
Science (Page 30)		
Scientific Enquiry	Investigate how to keep heat out.	Sc1/2b-m; Sc3/2c
	Investigate how to keep heat in.	Sc1/2b-m; Sc3/2c
Materials and Their Properties (QCA Science Unit 4C)	Recognise meaning of 'thermal conductor' and 'insulator'.	Sc3/1a-c
	Sort materials into thermal insulators and thermal conductors.	Sc3/1a-c
	Know that thermometers measure temperature in degrees.	Sc3/2c
Literacy (Page 32)		
Creating and Shaping Texts	Describe cold and hot weather.	En3/1b
	Compose cold and hot poems.	En3/1a-e;2a-e;12
	Make up similes.	En3/7a;9a
	Make a report of investigation into insulation.	En3/1a-e;10;12
	Research and write information booklets.	En3/1a-e;2a-f;6a,b; ICT PoS 1a-c
Understanding and Interpreting Texts	Find information about the Arctic and the Antarctic.	En2/5a-g
Speaking and Listening	Present information about a country; animal or person researched.	En1/1a-f;1/6a,c;1/8a-c; ICT1a-c;2a-c
	Devise relevant questions and answers about insulation.	En1/9b-c
	Review and comment on clothing for cold weather.	En1/9b-c
Mathematics (Page 34)		
Understanding Shape	Make hexagonal snowflakes.	Ma3/2a-c;4c
Measuring	Calculate measurements of ice balloons.	Ma3/1a;4e
	Measure and sequence temperatures.	Ma2/2a; Ma3/1a;4b
Handling Data	Construct and interpret bar graphs of data about temperature.	Ma4/2b,c
	Explain how graphs represent information.	ICT PoS 1b,c;2a;3b

Keeping Warm

Learning Objectives	Curriculum References
Design & Technology (Page 36)	
Make warm clothes for a cold penguin; choosing appropriate materials.	PoS 1a-d;2a-e;3a-c;4a,b;5a; QCA DT Unit 4A
Design and make a hot-water bottle cover	PoS 1a-d;2a-e;3a-c;4a,b;5a; QCA DT Unit 4A
Find out about feathers. Use appropriate materials to make one.	PoS 1a-d;2a-e;3a-c;4a,b;5a; QCA DT Unit 4A
Art (Page 36)	
Paint cold and hot pictures (link with poems in Literacy) using only black, white and one other colour.	PoS 1a-c;2c;3a,b;4a,b;5a
Examine and make repeated computer patterns for the Design & Technology designs for the penguin.	PoS 5c; ICT PoS 1a;2a;3a; QCA Art and Design Unit 3B
Music (Page 36)	
Devise music to accompany a silent DVD or video of cold and hot scenes.	PoS 2a,b
PE (Page 36)	
Copy the way animals/people move in cold/hot lands.	PoS 1a,b;2a-c;6a,b; QCA PE Unit 09
Re-enact the hatching of penguins into cold environment.	PoS 1a,b;2a-c;6a,b; QCA PE Unit 09
Devise a penguin parade moving carefully over ice and huddling together for warmth.	PoS 1a,b;2a-c;6a,b; QCA PE Unit 09
Geography (Page 38)	
Use a globe and world map to identify areas of hot and cold countries.	PoS 2c;3c,d,f
Compare and contrast Arctic and Antarctic conditions and animals.	PoS 2c,f;3a-g; QCA Geography Unit 24
Find out information about a cold or hot country and its people and animals.	PoS 3a-f: QCA Geography Unit 24
Compare temperature and rainfall in different countries in the world.	PoS 1a-c;3a
History (Page 38)	
Find out about exploration of cold and hot countries.	PoS 1;2c;4a,b;11
Research and present information about the conditions faced by explorers.	PoS 1;4a;5a-c
PSHCE (Page 38)	
Find out how the elderly are cared for in society in very cold weather.	PoS 5g,h

Keeping Warm

Science

Starting Points

● Introduce the term 'hypothesis' which explains a prediction, often using the word 'because'.

● Tell the children a story about a penguin who cannot stay warm. Discuss why he is cold (see the display above for ideas). Discuss the activity sheet on page 31. All three hypotheses given on the sheet use everyday knowledge as an explanation. If possible, encourage the use of scientific knowledge.

Enquiry

● Investigate the hypothesis on the Activity Sheet 'K-k-k-keep the penguin warm' on page 31, in pairs. Represent the body of a penguin with a drinks can containing warm water. Take the temperature of the water. Ensure that children know how to use a thermometer safely, how to read temperatures and take care of the thermometer so breakages don't happen. More able children may be able to use a temperature sensor rather than a thermometer to measure change.

> ⚠️ **SAFETY!**
> **Never use mercury thermometers with primary-aged children.**

● Introduce different materials such as foil, paper, cotton wool and other synthetic and natural fabrics. Put warm water into the cans. The children select at least three of the materials to wrap around the penguin's body. The materials may or may not be the same as those on the sheet. Sequence them into which the children predict will keep hotter for longest. Record predictions and hypothesise if possible, relating to experience or knowledge of the materials.

● Afterwards, as a class, sort the materials into two sets: 'thermal insulators' and 'thermal conductors'. Or sequence them from good to poor conductors of heat.

Extension Activities

● Ask groups to find out if colour affects how quickly water cools.

● Sequence materials that will stop an ice cube from melting for the longest time. Use the same materials as previously and find out if the results are the same as for keeping the water warm.

K-k-k-keep the penguin warm

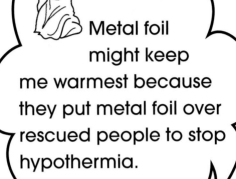 Metal foil might keep me warmest because they put metal foil over rescued people to stop hypothermia.

 Perhaps newspaper will keep me warmest because lots of sheets together make a thick material.

 I wonder if wool will be best because sheep have wool that keeps them warm in winter.

Which material do you think would be best? Let's test to find out!

You will need some cans of warm water and an adult to make sure what you do is safe.

Plan

1. What will you do?

2. What will you need?

3. How will you record what happens?

At the end

Which material is best?

Was your prediction correct?

Now you know!

Draw your penguin and dress it in the material that will keep him or her the warmest.

 **Does the colour of the material make a difference to how well it insulates the penguin?**

Literacy

Reading and Writing

- Encourage the children to write similes about cold and hot places such as 'as hot as the fiercest fiery flames' or 'as cold as the icy fingers of a stalactite'.

- Write icy poems in shivery or spiky writing.

- Read *Flapjack and Waddle* by Georgie Adams (Dolphin Books) which is a story about penguins for younger children. Explore how language and techniques are used to cause effect. Make up a 'cold' story for a younger child and illustrate it.

- Write a report on a scientific enquiry into insulation. This could be as a formal report or a cartoon to explain the stages. It could be by an individual or by groups for a wall display or presentation to other groups in the class.

- Research animals that live in cold or hot countries and write fact files or information leaflets (see the display above) and booklets about Arctic or Antarctic animals.

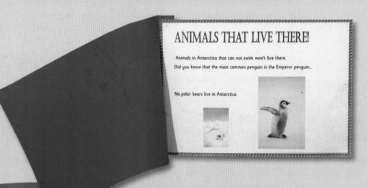

Speaking and Listening

- Devise other questions to ask about insulation and suggest ways of answering them to the children.

- Evaluate and discuss a range of clothing such as coats and footwear for wearing in cold weather, as on the activity sheet on page 33.

How good is it?

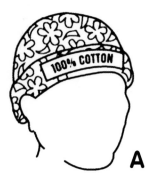 **A**
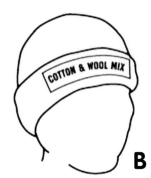 **B**
 **C**
 **D**

These are hats to wear in cold weather.

Write in the table what is good and what is not so good about each one.

	Good points	Not so good points
A		
B		
C		
D		

Which one would you wear in cold weather and why?

Write an advertisement for your chosen hat, persuading people that it is the best one they could buy. Think of an interesting way to present your information.

 Can you design a winter hat for yourself? What will it be made of? What will it look like? Make sure it is good at its job of keeping you warm.

Maths

Measuring

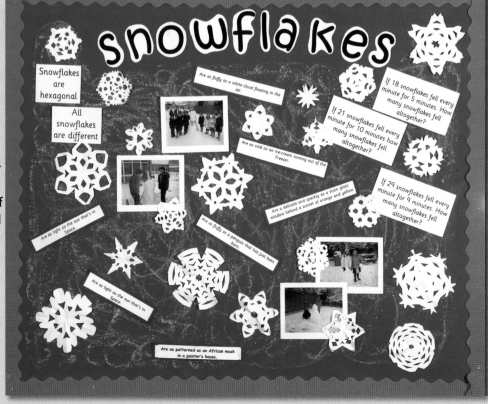

- Demonstrate how temperature is measured with an alcohol thermometer and how to treat the thermometer carefully. Name the parts of the thermometer and draw it for children to copy to show the sequence of numbers. Ask children to read the temperature in the room. Then ask what happens if they put a hand over the bulb at the bottom. The children should suggest why the temperature rises.

- Ask the children to estimate the temperature of a bowl of cold water using their hands and decide if it is colder or warmer than the room. Check by measuring the temperature. Ask them to estimate then measure other temperatures in different places in the room or the school.

 SAFETY!
Ensure no temperatures are too hot or cold.

- Make two ice balloons with the children. Fill each balloon with water by placing the nozzle of the balloon over the tap. Tie each, measure the circumferences and place them in a carrier bag each in a freezer. Remove them after two days. Take off the balloons to leave the shapes in ice. Measure the circumferences again. Explain that water expands on freezing. Relate this to burst pipes in winter. Observe the patterns in each ice balloon. Cloudy areas are where there is air trapped inside. Ask the children to devise questions about them. Do children think the ice balloons will sink or float? Relate the result to icebergs.

- Time how long an ice balloon takes to melt. Float one in a bowl of water and put another on a deep plate in the classroom. Take the temperature of the water and the room. Ask the children to predict what will happen to each balloon. Which will melt first? Measure the temperature near the balloons regularly. Put results on a pre-prepared table. Surprisingly the one in water melts faster. The reason being that a liquid has many more millions of molecules in contact with the ice than a gas like air.

Understanding Shape

- Show the children how to make snowflakes with six points as on the activity sheet on page 35. Display them alongside word problems about snowflakes for the children to solve (see the display above).

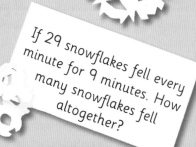

If 29 snowflakes fell every minute for 9 minutes. How many snowflakes fell altogether?

Handling Data

- Ask the children to take turns to measure the temperature outside each day for a week and record it on a class bar chart. They should then take turns to devise questions and answers about the bar chart.

Let's make snowflakes!

Snowflakes are amazing!

They all have six points.

They all have patterns.

To make snowflakes, this is what you do!

Draw around regular hexagon shapes of different sizes on a sheet of paper.

Cut out each hexagon.

Fold each into six equal parts like this.

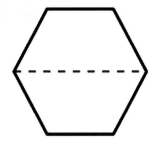  

Fold along dotted lines

Cut patterns along all the edges. Open up it up and compare it with a friend's snowflake.

Make sure that you leave a point at the top.

If you make several, all will be different – just like real snowflakes!

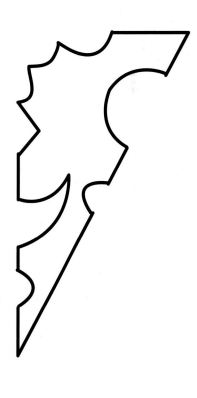

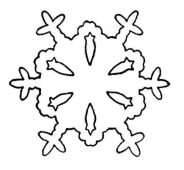

Design & Technology

- Provide materials such as cans, card, foil, paper, glues, colouring materials, fabrics and elastic bands. Challenge the children to make some warm clothes for a penguin who is always cold. They should choose materials and discuss their choice. They should realise that the clothes should allow as little heat as possible to escape.

- Find out about penguins in the cold weather and how they survive. Discuss the use of feathers and why they fluff up in cold weather. Observe the structures, textures and colours of a collection of feathers. Use senses to describe them. Provide a variety of materials for the children to make their own feather. Include some that are not appropriate, such as modelling clay, thin fabrics and foil.

- Discuss the properties of hot-water bottle covers and oven mitts. Discuss the materials used and their design. Ask the children to plan and design a hot-water bottle cover choosing their own materials. See the activity sheet on page 37.

Art

- Use a computer package to design some repeated patterns for a penguin coat. Use this for a class display called 'The Penguin Fashion Show' (as shown in the display above).

- Encourage the children to paint hot and cold pictures. Provide only black, white and another colour. The children should close their eyes and envisage what their picture may look like. Encourage the use of cold and hot shapes and mixing of colours to make shades. It could be a scene or a design but should be clear whether it represents hot or cold.

Music

- Watch a silent DVD or video of a cold or hot scene: include a snowstorm, desert, fire, or scenery in a cold or hot climate. The children could make sounds with their voices and bodies to accompany a chosen scene. Work in groups to create a sequence and add sounds from instruments to accompany the scene. They should practise and review their accompaniments.

PE

- Play 'follow the leader' to devise a penguin parade, where penguins move on land towards the sea.

- Act out the hatching of a penguin showing the struggle to break open the egg and learning to move on the slippery ice, until they get used to it.

Keeping Warm

Keeping us warm

Look at a hot-water bottle. It won't stay warm for long but a cover for the hot-water bottle could make it stay warm for longer.

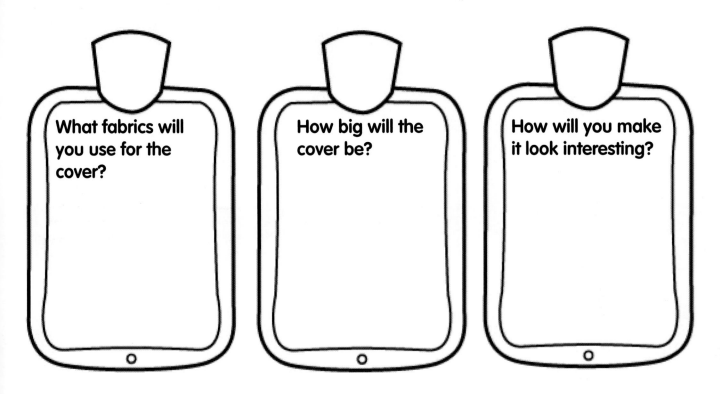

What fabrics will you use for the cover?

How big will the cover be?

How will you make it look interesting?

Write your ideas on the hot-water bottles.

Now make a cover.

1. Cut out a paper shape for the cover. Make sure the actual hot water bottle will fit inside the shape.

2. On the paper shape write the properties of your cover: size, materials, shape, colours and design and anything else you can think of.

3. Use your information to choose a suitable fabric for the cover.

4. Cut out two paper shapes from the fabric.

5. Decide the best way to join the two shapes together at the edges.

6. Decide on a way to fasten the top of the cover.

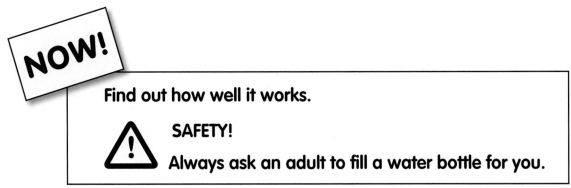

NOW!

Find out how well it works.

⚠️ **SAFETY!**
Always ask an adult to fill a water bottle for you.

Geography

- Find out the similarities and differences between the Arctic and the Antarctic. Ask the children to research animals living in each place. Draw and paint them as accurately as possible and add information to make a display. Down one side of the display, list the similarities and on the other list the differences. See the activity sheet on page 39.

- On a globe, identify selected areas of hot and cold countries. Use the vocabulary for direction and names of parts of the world, such as 'equator', 'poles', 'tropics', 'island', 'country' and so on.

- Find out about people and their way of life in a cold or hot country such as Inuits from the Arctic or people of the desert. Use books and the Internet to find information.

History

- Research exploration of cold and hot countries from earliest times to the present day. Findings could be written on a timeline. They could include Scott of the Antarctic (1868–1912), Roald Amundsen (1872–1928) and Dr David Livingstone (1813–1873). Identify where they travelled on a globe or world map.

- Compose letters from an explorer to home to explain the conditions they are facing and any other important information or write a newspaper report of their findings. Use secondary sources for information.

- Compare temperature and rainfall in different countries of the world.

PSHCE

- Discuss the dangers for elderly people in very cold weather. Encourage the children to devise ways that they could keep warm even if they do not have much money to spend. Find some data about how elderly people in the United Kingdom are helped by the government in very cold weather.

> I am a penguin.
> There are 17 different kinds of penguins in the Antarctic, like the Emperor, the rock hopper and the macaroni.
> We are all very good swimmers so people used to think we were fish. We can't fly but we are definitely birds because we have wings and feathers.
> The one you see most is the king penguin.
> It is the second largest after the Emperor penguin.
> All of us eat krill that are like shrimps, fish and squid.
> We have to watch out for sharks and leopard seals because they like a nice, juicy penguin for their lunch.

Keeping Warm

The Arctic and the Antarctic

Find out some similarities and differences between the Arctic and the Antarctic.

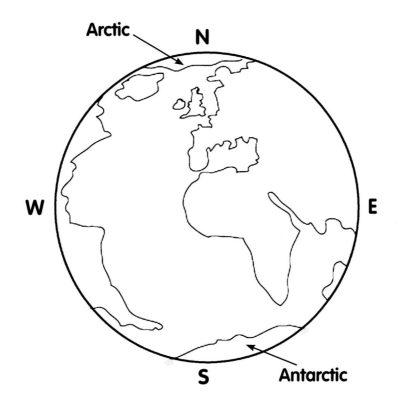

Similarities	Differences

Solids and Liquids

These grids demonstrate the learning objectives covered in the activities within the theme. The curriculum references indicate the relevant programme of study (PoS) for a subject area unless otherwise stated.

	Learning Objectives	Curriculum References
Science (Page 42)		
Scientific Enquiry	Think creatively to solve a problem to separate a mixture.	Sc1/1a
	Select and use equipment to separate materials.	Sc1/2c;e
Physical Processes (QCA Science Unit 4D)	Know main differences between solids; liquids and gases.	Sc3/1e
	Describe the changes that happen when materials	Sc3/2a
	Recognise the processes of dissolving.	Sc3/2d
	Know how to separate mixtures by sieving and filtering.	Sc3/3a;c
	Begin to understand the process of evaporation in everyday events.	Sc3/2d
Literacy (Page 44)		
Group Discussion and Interaction	Identify liquids and solids from clues.	En1/1a,c;2a
Understanding and Interpreting Texts	Read about the manufacture of tea and coffee.	En2/3a-c
Engaging With and Responding to Texts	Read myths and legends and understand how they describe events.	En2/2a-d;3a-d;4a-c
Creating and Shaping Texts	Write instructions about how to make a cup of tea.	En3/1a-e;6a
	Devise leaflets about manufacture of tea and/or coffee.	En3/1a-e;2a-f
	Make up short poems to describe and name solids; liquids and gases.	En3/1a-e;12
	Find solids; liquids and gases for each letter of the alphabet.	En3/1a-e;2a-f;6a
Mathematics (Page 46)		
Using and Applying Mathematics	Find volumes of different containers.	Ma3/1a,c,g;4a,b
	Measure volumes of small solids.	Ma3/1a,c,g;4a,b
Measuring	Select and use appropriate equipment for measuring different things.	Ma3/1a,d;4a,b
	Measure and compare volumes in different containers.	Ma3/1a,d;4a,b
	Complete missing numbers on measuring scales.	Ma2/1k;2a,i
	Measure volumes of solids and liquids.	Ma3/1a,d;4a,b
	Measure time to the nearest minute and calculate time intervals.	Ma3/1a;4d

Solids and Liquids

Learning Objectives	Curriculum References
Design & Technology (Page 48)	
Make sieves to separate a mixture of solids.	PoS 1a-d;2a,b;3a-c
Study a range of natural and manufactured containers for different foodstuffs and list their properties.	PoS 1a-d;2a-e;3a-c; 4a;5b,c
Design and make a container for carrying a liquid.	PoS 1a-d;2a-e;3a-c;4a;5b-c; QCA DT Unit 4A
PE (Page 48)	
Move in water in different ways and compare with movement on land..	PoS 9a-d
History (Page 48)	
Decide how and why the local area developed on its site.	PoS 1a,b;2a,b;3a,b; 4a,b;5a-c
Study Egyptian civilizasion which developed on the River Nile.	PoS 1a,b;2a;3a,b;4a,b;5a-c; QCA History Unit 10
Art (Page 50)	
Design and make mobiles about liquids and solids; painting with watercolour using no brushes.	PoS 1c;2a,c;3a,b;4a-c;5a-d
Make up oil paints to paint items for mobiles.	PoS 1c;2a,c;3a,b;4a-c;5a-d
Make a display of solids, liquids and gases.	PoS 1c;2a,c;3a,b;4a-c;5a-d
Music (Page 50)	
Identify instruments that are played by solids hitting together and by air (gases) vibrating.	PoS 4c
Make and play a 'bottle' keyboard.	PoS 4b,c
Geography (Page 50)	
Study locations of villages on a map. Consider why they grew up on that site.	PoS 1a-e;2a-f;3e,f;6c-e
Make up an imaginary village and draw keys.	PoS 2e,g
Consider the ways of life of people in the world and the importance of water to them – a village in India or the Inuits in the Arctic.	PoS 1a-c;2a,c,d,f;3a-g; 4a,b;5a,b
RE (Page 50)	
Read the Hindu story of Svetaketu and the cup of salty water and understand how it relates to the Hindu teaching about God.	PoS 3b,f; QCA RE Unit 4A

Solids and Liquids

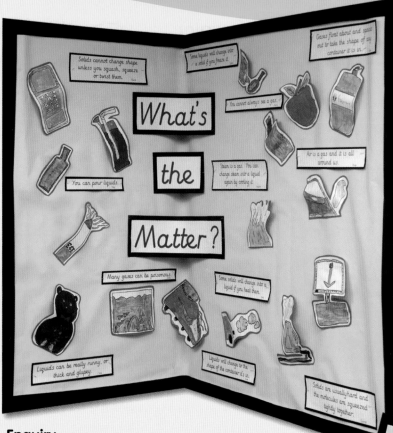

Starting Points

- Show a range of solids and liquids. Include less obvious ones, such as syrup, jelly, sand, salt, cotton wool and even toothpaste. Ask groups to sort them into solids and liquids and come to an agreement. Children may think that solids have to be hard, in which case cotton wool does not fit in with their hypothesis. Difficult ones are jelly and toothpaste, neither of which are true solids or liquids. However, leaving a strip of toothpaste out for a while will show that it does change shape. Try this with other doubtful substances. Make up rules to define a solid and a liquid. Record results such as on the display.

Enquiry

- Investigate separating mixtures of solids, and mixtures of solids with liquids. Suggest the following mixtures: marbles and paperclips in flour; rice in icing sugar; sand and salt in water. Ask the children to suggest others.

- Discuss in groups what can be done to separate the mixtures. Provide suitable equipment, such as magnets, filter paper, jugs, containers, and sieves which can be home-made (see the activity sheet on page 49) or bought ones. The children can record group ideas, then test them to see which groups manage to separate their ingredients.

- Discuss afterwards the methods used and name the processes such as using magnets, sieving, filtering and evaporation.

Extension Activities

- In groups, find out which of a collection of ingredients dissolve and which do not. Include rice, salt, brown sugar, flour, coffee and chocolate. Record the results on a prepared table as on the activity sheet on page 43. Some children may devise their own table. Introduce the vocabulary of 'dissolve', 'soluble', 'insoluble', and 'solution'. Discuss how materials that dissolve may be recovered by evaporation.

You can pour liquids.
Jay

Does it dissolve?

Tom wanted to find out if different foods dissolve in water. He made up a table like the one below. He predicted that coffee would dissolve, then he tried it out and wrote the results in the table.

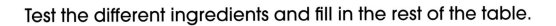

Test the different ingredients and fill in the rest of the table.

Food	Prediction ✔ yes	Prediction ✘ no	Test yes	Test no
Rice				
Icing sugar				
Salt				
Brown sugar				
Coffee	✔		✔	
Chocolate				

Reading and Writing

- Show the children how to make a cup of tea. Teach them how to write instructions using connecting words to start each sentence such as 'First', 'Then', 'Next' and 'Finally' and so on, as on the activity sheet on page 45. Identify the solids, liquids and gases involved in making a cup of tea as on the display.

- Read about the growing and preparing of coffee beans and tea leaves, how they are manufactured and when they became popular. Compare ways of making coffee and tea. Groups could create information leaflets.

- Devise short poems using examples of solids, liquids and gases.

- Write a recipe as a page for a cookery book, for a celebration, showing ingredients, method and decoration. Highlight ingredients that are solids or liquids in different colours.

- Play the alphabet game. Ask pairs of children to find a solid and a liquid beginning with each letter of the alphabet. Or give the children one minute to write down all the liquids they can think of. Another pair check the list.

- Provide a description which has different solids and liquids in it. Ask the children to circle all the solids in red and the liquids in blue.

- Read stories from legends, such as the Greek story of Daedalus and his wax wings. Write a paragraph about Daedalus and how he felt.

Speaking and Listening

- Play the 'What is it?' game. Provide a large box containing a variety of items that are solids or liquids. Children sit back to back with a partner. One of them collects one thing from the collection and gives three clues about it using their senses and/or knowledge for the other to guess. Reverse the roles. How many can each pair get through in a limited time?

Tea with Grandma

Jane is visiting Grandma.

"Put the kettle on, Jane," says Grandma. "Let's have a nice cup of tea. The tea and sugar are on the shelf, milk in the jug. Oh, and don't forget to strain out all the tea leaves will you dear," she called.

OH DEAR! There is a problem! Jane has no idea how to make a cup of tea.

Write instructions for each stage for her here.

Use words to start each sentence to connect them, such as: **First, Then, Next, After that, Lastly** or **Finally**

The first sentence has been written for you.

First you put water in the kettle and switch it on.

Using and Applying

- Ask the children to pick up a handful of small solid objects, such as grains of rice or breakfast cereal and find the volume of them by transferring them to a measuring jug or cylinder. Find out who can pick up the greatest volume in one hand. Does that child have the biggest hand?

- Provide children with a bottle of coloured water and other containers of different shapes. Ask them to draw where they think the level of the liquid will be in the new container.

- Learn the meanings of 'milli' and 'centi' in measurement and use these in measuring familiar things in and outside the classroom.

Measuring

- Show a range of items such as a book, a rug, some water and other liquids, an apple, a tin of peas and other containers of food, both solid and liquid. Ask the children what measurements they would want to know about each of the items. Ask what instruments the children would use to measure them. Provide various instruments for them to choose from such as rulers, measuring tapes, trundle wheels, different types of weighing scales including spring balances, measuring jugs and cylinders of different volumes. Create a display of measuring instruments. Sort their questions into 'mass' (children may want to use 'weight' at this stage as they will be uncertain of the difference between mass and weight), 'length' (which includes width and depth) and 'volume'.

- Let the children measure each item after estimating first. Practice any of the measurements that cause a problem.

- Show children a bottle containing some coloured water. Cover the bottle and tilt it. Ask them to draw the level of the liquid inside. Repeat for different angles. The children should compare the results with their predictions. They should notice that the level of the liquid is always parallel to the ground.

- Show children a range of measuring scales with some measurements missing for them to complete.

- Use the activity sheet on page 47 to give the children practice in measuring time.

What's cooking?

Read the instructions on the notepad.
These are the times that different
children put their biscuits in the oven
and when they took them out.

IN   **OUT**

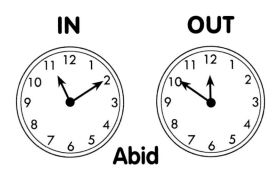

Abid

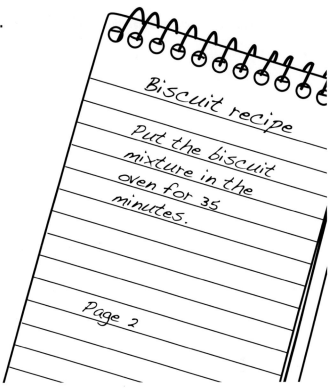

Biscuit recipe

Put the biscuit
mixture in the
oven for 35
minutes.

Page 2

Peter

Whose biscuits will be just right?

_____

Whose will be burned black?

_____

Whose will still be a bit soggy?

_____

Jon

Ann

NOW!

If Jake puts his biscuits in the
oven at this time, complete
the other clock to show when
he should take them out.

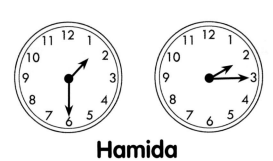

Hamida

Design & Technology

- Make a series of sieves to separate a collection of different sized solids, such as marbles, sand, breakfast cereal and rice as on the activity sheet on page 49. The children should decide on the size of the holes and the order of the sieves to do the job. Display these along with other methods of separating solids and separating liquids from solids (see page 42).

> ⚠️ **SAFETY!**
> **Children must know how to use sharp instruments safely!**

- Use the sieves in a problem to separate sand and other things from water. This could link with a problem of obtaining water to drink in a village settlement in Geography (see page 50).

- Study a variety of containers, both natural and manufactured, such as bags, pods of seeds, purses, bottles and so on and list their properties.

- Design containers for holding liquids. Decide what their special properties are. They could make a container from found materials for a particular purpose and decorate it using appropriate materials. The children will need to use waterproof materials or find ways of making a material waterproof, such as by coating in PVA glue.

PE

- During swimming lessons, ask the children to move in different ways and compare it with movement on land.

History

- Study the local area and find out how it has changed. Link with Geography, using questions such as *'Was there a natural water supply?'* Compare the area as it is now with a certain time in the past.

- Study the Egyptian civilisation which developed on the River Nile and investigate all aspects of their life such as food, clothing, beliefs about life after death and how they prepared for it.

Separate them!

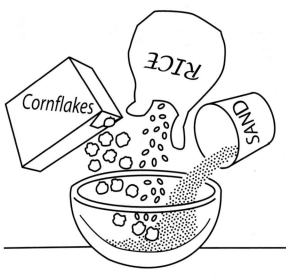

How could you separate the cornflakes, rice and sand from this mixture? They are all different sizes so you could pick out the cornflakes and the rice grains one by one. But this would take too long.

Make sieves with different sized holes from some of the equipment in the pictures. Plan how to do it and what equipment you may need.

Plastic

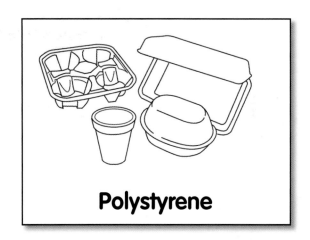

Polystyrene

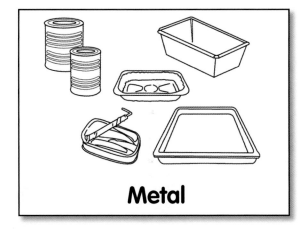

Metal

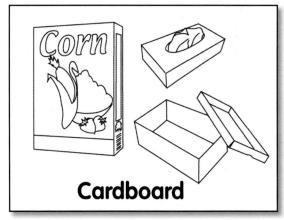

Cardboard

How many sieves did you need?

Describe what you did in words and diagrams.

Did the sieves work?
Could you improve what you did?

Art

- Design mobiles depicting either solids or liquids. Paint the items for the mobile with water colours using no brushes. Use fingers, sponges, sticks and so on and experiment with mixing colours and with shapes for effect.

- Let children mix powder paint and oil and paint objects for the mobiles with these oil paints. Compare the effects of watercolours and oils.

- Make a display of the solids, liquids and gases identified when making a cup of tea (see page 44).

Music

- Discuss how instruments produce music in different ways. Identify instruments that make sounds by air passing through (them (such as wind instruments) and ones that make sounds by solids hitting together (such as percussion or stringed instruments). Make instruments from found items as in the display above.

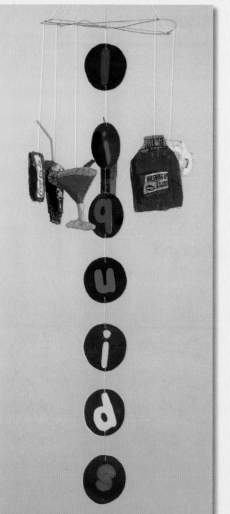

- Make and play a 'bottle' keyboard. The bottles need to be all the same size and filled with varying amounts of water graduating from empty to full or different sized bottles with equal amounts of water. Experiment to find the best 'drumstick' to tap the bottles with and to discover what sounds are made when air is blown into them.

Geography

- Study locations of villages on a map. Discuss why they grew up on this site. Note that many grew up around rivers and streams because they were a way of transporting goods and building materials.

- Find out about the ways of life of people in the world such as a village in India or an Inuit settlement in the Arctic. Consider the importance of water to them and the difficulty they may have obtaining fresh water to drink.

- Ask children to devise their own plan of a village settlement around a water route. They should use their own map symbols and draw a key (see the activity sheet on page 51). Use the village as a starting point for literacy, numeracy and technology activities.

RE

- Read the Hindu story of Svetaketu and his glass of water with salt added. Hindus teach that, like salt in water, God is invisible but is there in everything.

The first settler

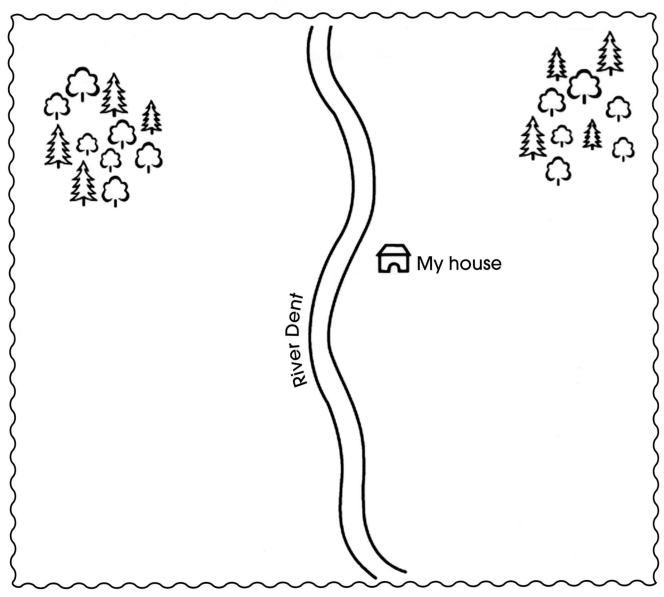

This is my house. I am the first settler here.

The rest of my clan want to leave their village to join me.

Complete the village plan for us all.

What will we need so that we can live, grow some crops and have places to enjoy ourselves?

What other things would you put in our village?

Finish the key so that it makes sense to everyone who reads it.

Friction

These grids demonstrate the learning objectives covered in the activities within the theme. The curriculum references indicate the relevant programme of study (PoS) for a subject area unless otherwise stated.

	Learning Objectives	Curriculum References
Science (Page 54)		
Scientific Enquiry	Compare friction on different surfaces.	Sc1/2a-m
Physical Processes (QCA Science Unit 4E)	Identify where forces are acting on moving things.	Sc4/2c
	Identify friction as a force trying to stop things from moving.	Sc4/2c
	Identify the direction of friction on different moving things.	Sc4/2c,e
Literacy (Page 56)		
Speaking	Present own work about friction with an audience in mind.	En1/3a-c
	Relate, explain and evaluate different books.	En1/1a-f
Group Discussion and Interaction	Critically evaluate work of others in the class about friction; in pairs, groups and whole class.	En1/2a-e;3a-e
	Participate in designing and presenting a class assembly about moving things.	En1/1a-e
Understanding and Interpreting Texts	Read about different forms of transport and how they work.	En2/3a-f
	Read poems about moving along on different forms of transport.	En2/4a,f
Engaging with and Responding to Texts	Read and explain events about Mrs Armitage and her adventures on her bicycle.	En2/4c
Creating and Shaping Texts	Make up poems about things travelling through the air, on land and in water.	En3/2a-f;12
	Describe feelings when travelling at speed.	En3/1a-e
Mathematics (Page 58)		
Using and Applying Mathematics	Calculate cost of journeys and holidays.	Ma2/1a-d;4a,d
	Read timetables and calculate times from them.	Ma2/1a-d;4a,d
	Calculate savings for special offers on journeys and holidays.	Ma2/1a-d;4a,d
	Explore ways of timing how long different shapes take to fall to the ground.	Ma3/4d
Calculating	Calculate equations.	Ma2/3a,d,f,g,h
	Devise equations for others to calculate.	Ma2/3a,d,f,g,h
Measuring	Measure time in minutes, seconds, and am and pm.	Ma3/4d
Handling Data	Record results of a slow bicycle race; collect and display data.	ICT PoS 1a-c;3b
	Present information in various ways about the friction theme.	ICT PoS 1a-c;3a,b

Friction

Learning Objectives	Curriculum References
Design & Technology (Page 60)	
Explore the gears on a bicycle and make up own systems.	PoS 5a,b
Design and make a moving fruit or vegetable vehicle.	PoS 1a-d;2a-f;3a-c;4a,b
Test distances travelled by made buggies.	PoS 1a-d; 2a-f; 3a-c; 4a,b
Art (Page 60)	
Design decorative wheels and combine into patterns.	PoS 2a-c; QCA Art & Design Unit 4C
Design a book cover about transport or friction.	PoS 1a,b;4a,b
PE (Page 60)	
Identify where friction is acting when swimming.	PoS 9a-d; QCA PE Unit16
Compare the soles of sports shoes.	PoS 2a-c;3a,b
Geography (Page 62)	
Find out about transport in different parts of the world.	PoS 1a,b;3a-d;4a,b
Find out how children travel about.	PoS 1a-c; QCA Geography Units19;25; ICT PoS 1a-c; QCA ICT Unit 4D
History (Page 62)	
Find out the history of the bicycle, car, aeroplane or train.	PoS 1a,b;4a,b
Find out about the lives of Roman, Viking or Anglo-Saxon settlers in Britain and how they travelled.	PoS 1a,b;2a,c,d; QCA History Units 6A; 6B or 6C
Find out about disasters at sea and in the air and famous rescues.	PoS 1a,b;2a,c,d
Put past events on a timeline.	PoS 1a,b
PSHCE (Page 62)	
Understand the rules for personal safety on the roads.	PoS 2b,3e,5a; QCA Citizenship Unit 08
Know how to care for bicycles.	PoS 2b;3e;5a
Music (Page 62)	
Know how friction acts when playing different instruments.	PoS 1b
Explore and represent the rhythm of a train and/or other transport.	PoS 4a-e;3a-c; QCA Music Unit 10

Friction

Starting Points

● Remind the children that a force is a push or a pull. Show examples such as putting magnets together, stretching and pushing springs, pulling and pushing heavy and light objects and dropping objects. Identify forces and their size and direction. Write down force facts.

● Explain friction as a force that happens when you try to move one surface over another. Ask the children to rub their hands together gently and gradually harder until they feel how difficult it gets to move them, and that they get hot. Friction acts against the direction of movement and produces heat. Study the soles of shoes and discuss how they are useful in stopping us sliding about. Some have more friction between them and a surface than others.

Enquiry

● Investigate the grip of shoes. Select shoes with different types of soles from smooth to rough and of different patterns. Let the children make rubbings of soles and put the rubbings into a predicted order of grip, suggesting why. The children could test their predictions in one of these three ways.

1. Place each shoe on a PE bench. Add a mass of 200g to represent a person's foot inside it. Raise the bench **(do not allow a child to do this)** until the shoe slips. Measure the height of the end of the bench for each shoe tested.

2. Attach a thick elastic band to the shoes in turn and pull them along a flat surface. Measure how much the band stretches to move the shoe.

3. Look at a forcemeter and talk to the children about how it works. Measure the force needed to get each shoe (with the mass inside it) to start moving on a flat surface. Get the children to record the results on a table. Ask them to decide what type of graph is possible using the data. Link the properties of shoes to how and when we use them.

● Compare the force needed when different masses are placed inside the shoe when on surfaces of different roughness. Make up a generalised statement that 'the heavier the shoe, the more mass, the greater the force needed, the more the friction'. Some children will not be able to generalise at this stage but will be able to say what happens for each one.

Extension Activities

● Discuss examples of when friction is useful (on tyres and shoes) and when not (parts of machinery which wear out).

● Look at pictures of forces in action and identify direction and names of forces as on the display above and on the activity sheet on page 55.

Where's the friction?

Here are pictures of some moving things. The arrows show you in which direction they are moving.

Draw another arrow on each picture to show the direction of friction on each of these moving things.

NOW!

Joe and Jack are running as fast as they can. Draw an arrow to show the direction they are moving.

Draw another arrow to show the direction of friction on them.

Label the two arrows.

Joe cannot run as fast holding the card in front of him. Why?

thin card

Reading and Writing

- Make up 'What am I?' quiz poems for things that cause friction (water, air and land) as in the display above and the activity sheet on page 57.

- Show images of objects moving. Ask the children to write verbs and adjectives to describe them; then to put the words together in similes and metaphors. These could be expanded into poems or short descriptive writing.

- Read stories about *Mrs Armitage* by Quentin Blake (Red Fox). Tell or write a review of one of the books. Discuss imaginary adventures with bicycles.

- Devise a friction character and make up a story about how it tries to stop something moving. It could be a hero stopping a runaway vehicle or a villain making someone lose a race.

- Find and evaluate information about bicycles or other forms of transport in books, such as *Cycling in action* (Sports in action series) by John Crossingham (Crabtree). Give children four blank pages for them to write their own information book, including a glossary of terms and an index. They need to plan first, with help. If they need more room, they need to consider how to add inserts – but their book must only be four pages long. This helps them to plan use of space more effectively. You might want to make the pages even fewer.

Speaking and Listening

- Read 'From a railway carriage' by R. L. Stevenson from *A child's garden of verse* (Puffin Books). Encourage the children to make up a rhythm to recite it to. Some of the class could make background sounds of the rhythm of the train and different groups could speak different rhyming couplets. For example:

  'Rickety rack, trickery track
  Down the line with the wind on my back

  Whistle is blowing whoo-oo-oo-oo
  Where in the world are you going to?'

- Make up a class assembly about moving things to include different subjects: scientific information, poems, safety, records of speed, amazing facts and so on.

What am I?

I'm every where but you cannot see me you are always with me.
Whirling around your head and whispering in your ear.
I am always with you but you can't see me.
I am invisible and invincible.
Peaceful, mighty and magical.
I soften the creases of your skin
And with breath I am where life can begin

Hope, Luke, William & Rachel

Moving poetry

When you write a poem you need to think about how you want the reader to feel and then choose words to help get that feeling. It needs to paint a picture.

Read this poem.

I **go on** water
Moving along;
Moving along;
Then coming back
I am **quiet**
Passing by
I am like a **ghost**
What am I?

A steamboat, a swimmer or a yacht? It could be any of these. This is an OK poem but …it does not really paint an interesting picture. It could be so much better.

Write it out, changing the words in bold either into other words or by adding to them to make it more interesting.

NOW!

Choose a moving thing of your own and write your own eight line poem on a separate sheet of paper.

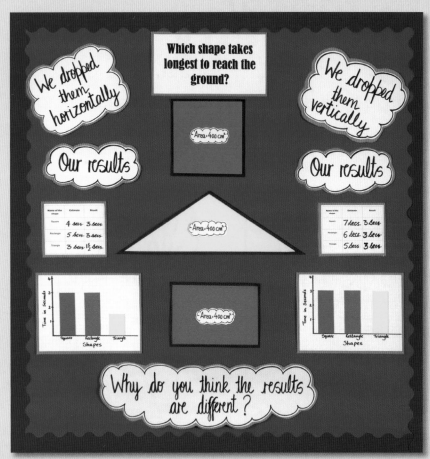

Using and Applying

- Make up a hexagon, triangle, square and other rectangles with the same area using geoboards and elastic bands. Some will have to be approximate. Transfer the areas to squared paper. Drop each shape from a set height in turn, first estimating and then measuring with a stopwatch to compare the falling times. (Link with Science and parachutes.) Is there a difference? Does it make a difference how the shape is dropped? Display the results as shown.

- Look at timetables for buses or trains. Calculate the time taken for journeys and explain why there is a difference for similar journeys. Take the class on a journey and ask them to time it.

- Find out the price of tickets for certain journeys and calculate how much it would be for the family to go on the journey.

- Look in the newspaper for costs of holidays. Find out what the holiday includes: meals, transport, visits and so on. Calculate the cost for a family to go.

Calculating

- Calculate sums such as those on the activity sheet on page 59.

- Devise similar sums for others to calculate.

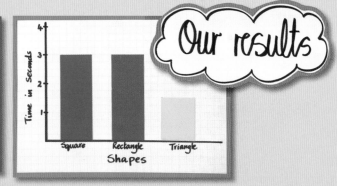

Name of the shape	Estimate	Result
Square	4 secs.	3 secs
Rectangle	5 secs.	3 secs.
Triangle	3 secs.	1½ secs.

Measuring

- Hold a 'slow' bicycle race. Plot the course in the playground and measure the distance. Time people to find out whether or not they get faster with practice.

Handling Data

- Find ways to advertise and display the results of the 'slow' bicycle race.

- Record the results of children running a distance with and without a large card area held in front of them (see the activity sheet on page 55) .This involves measuring time and plotting two bar graphs for each child: with and without card.

- Ask groups to make up their own advertisements for a journey including the cost and special offers.

Try these!

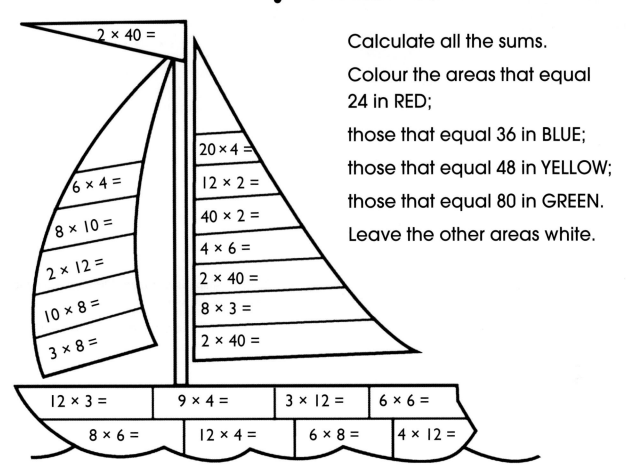

Calculate all the sums.

Colour the areas that equal 24 in RED;

those that equal 36 in BLUE;

those that equal 48 in YELLOW;

those that equal 80 in GREEN.

Leave the other areas white.

Sail equations:
2 × 40 =

6 × 4 =
8 × 10 =
2 × 12 =
10 × 8 =
3 × 8 =

20 × 4 =
12 × 2 =
40 × 2 =
4 × 6 =
2 × 40 =
8 × 3 =
2 × 40 =

Boat equations:
12 × 3 =   9 × 4 =   3 × 12 =   6 × 6 =
8 × 6 =   12 × 4 =   6 × 8 =   4 × 12 =

If that was easy, now try this one.

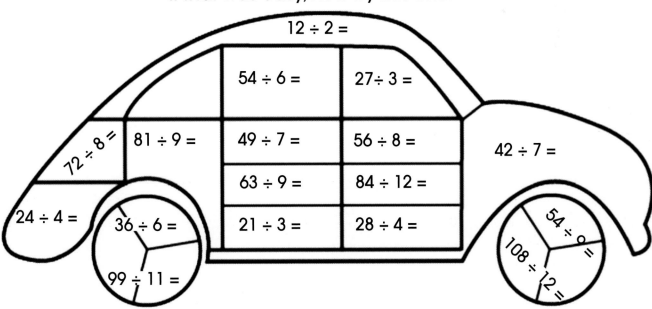

Car equations:
12 ÷ 2 =
54 ÷ 6 =   27 ÷ 3 =
72 ÷ 8 =   81 ÷ 9 =   49 ÷ 7 =   56 ÷ 8 =   42 ÷ 7 =
63 ÷ 9 =   84 ÷ 12 =
24 ÷ 4 =   36 ÷ 6 =   21 ÷ 3 =   28 ÷ 4 =   54 ÷ 9 =
99 ÷ 11 =   108 ÷ 12 =

Calculate all the sums.

Colour the areas that equal 6 in RED;

those that equal 9 in BLUE;

those that equal 7 in YELLOW.

Leave the other areas white.

Design & Technology

- Look at bicycles. Identify danger points. Discuss how to look after a bicycle (see the display) and talk about how friction is useful on a bicycle when using the brakes, for tyres on the road, for feet on pedals and hands on handlebars. Talk about where friction is not useful – between the gears. Examine gears on bicycles. Whilst riding, change gears to see what happens.

- Use a large carrot to make a carrot car as on the activity sheet on page 61.

> ⚠️ **SAFETY!** Only an adult should use a sharp knife to cut the carrot.

- Make simple buggies from thick card and attach plastic lids from jars and bottles for wheels so they will rotate. Time how long each buggy takes to go down a slope or measure how far it travels from the end of the slope. Compare distances travelled when elastic band tyres are added. Relate this to the use of tyres on real bicycles and cars.

Art

- Look at the design of all sorts of wheels around us: on vehicles, at the fairground and in machines. Collect circular boxes and lids of containers and decorate inside and out, using card, paper and foils and paints and pastels, or use textiles and stitch wheel patterns. Arrange the decorated wheels in groups to make colourful displays.

- Look at the style of art work of Quentin Blake (b.1932), who illustrated the 'Mr Gumpy' books (Henry Holt and Co) and many of the books of Roald Dahl (1916–1990). Discuss what is distinctive about his style. Try to make up a style like his or use a different style to illustrate a book cover on the subject of friction or a story about movement.

PE

- When swimming, ask the children to feel friction acting when they are moving through water. Consider if it would be easier or more difficult moving through oil or washing up liquid and consider why.

- Compare the soles of shoes used for different sports. Discuss and decide why each shoe is best for its sport.

Make a carrot car

You will need:

A board to work on

A large carrot (cleaned)

Two cocktail sticks

A skewer to make a small hole in the side of the carrots

A knife (**If you are allowed to use a knife be very careful.**) ⚠️

An adult to help you

Lots of care!

What to do:

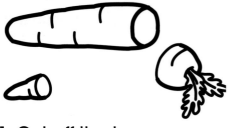

1. Cut off the two ends of the carrot.

2. Then cut off four equal pieces for the wheels.

3. Make two holes through the carrot for the cocktail sticks (the axles).

4. Push the cocktail sticks through the holes and attach the wheels.

5. Shape the carrot further if you like.

6. Now try out your car. Do the wheels move around?

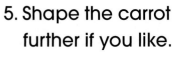

Design and make another vegetable or fruit buggy.

It headed for action in 1545 against the French Fleet. The warship sank in the Solent with up to 700 men on board.

It went to war between 1512 - 1522. It was one of the first ships able to fire a broadside.

It was recovered from the sea bed in 1982. It had 2000 artefacts found on board. This has created a unique picture of Tudor life at sea.

The Mary Rose was built between 1509 - 1511. It was launched in 1511. It was King Henry VIII's favourite ship.

Henry VIII (1491-1547)

Time Line

Life of the Mary Rose

Geography

- Discuss the different ways the children have travelled over the last week such as on foot, by bicycle, by car, on roller skates, by train and so on. Discuss the friction found on these methods of transport. Draw a map of 'My journey to school'.

- Find out about transport in different parts of the world. They could research particular ways of travel in different countries, for example rickshaws in Asia, monorails in USA, trams in Nottingham and so on.

History

- Find out about ships and sailors in the past such as the Romans and Viking and Anglo-Saxon ships. Can the children show where friction is found on ships in the water? This could develop into a study of these past ways of life. Observe actual artefacts from the time at a museum and use the artefacts to ask historical questions and find out more information.

- Focus on specific events in a historical period, for example the Spanish Armada and the *Mary Rose* in Tudor times (see the display above.) In the displays (below and right) the boat has been made to lift up to show the interior underneath. Famous rescues such as that by Grace Darling, and disasters at sea such as the sinking of the *Lusitania* or the *Titanic* could be studied..

PSHCE

- Act out crossing the road. Discuss what things are important when outside walking or cycling. Remind the children about the Green Cross Code. Discuss the rules of travelling on the road and the reasons for them. Discuss rules and laws in general and why they are needed (see the activity sheet on page 63).

- Find out about safety for bikes and about road safety.

Music

- Identify where there is friction when playing different instruments, for example bowing or plucking with fingers on strings; scraping a glockenspiel; rubbing wood blocks and so on.

- Ask the children to tap out the rhythm of a train moving using the instruments. Add words to describe the music. Make up a song or spoken poem by having a chorus for the beat such as 'Clickety clack, rickety rack' while words are sung or spoken over it and the music beat accompanies it.

In the street

Put a circle around the people who are not being careful in this picture.

Write what each one is doing wrong.

_____

_____

_____

_____

_____

_____

Circuits and Conductors

These grids demonstrate the learning objectives covered in the activities within the theme. The curriculum references indicate the relevant programme of study (PoS) for a subject area unless otherwise stated.

	Learning Objectives	Curriculum References
Science (Page 66)		
Scientific Enquiry	Find a variety of ways to construct an electrical circuit.	Sc1/1a;2a-m
	Test materials for electrical conductivity.	Sc1/1b;2b,c,e,f,g,h,i,j,k,l,m
	Explain how electricity travels through a bulb.	Sc1/2e
Physical Processes (QCA Science Unit 4F)	Construct circuits with batteries, bulbs, motors and buzzers.	Sc4/1a
	Know about safety when using electricity.	Sc1/2e; Breadth of Study 2b
	Know that there are different sizes and strengths of batteries.	Sc4/1a
	Know that a complete circuit is needed for appliances to work.	Sc4/1a
Materials and Their Properties	Sort materials into good and poor conductors of electricity.	Sc3/1c
	Identify materials that are good or poor conductors of electricity.	Sc3/1c
Literacy (Page 68)		
Speaking	Discuss and present information about *The iron man* (by Ted Hughes) to others.	En1/1b-e;8b
Listening and Responding	Discuss an imaginary silver man.	En1/2b,e;3c;9a
	Describe imaginary or real machines and how they work.	En3/1a-e;2a-e; 5a,b;9a
Creating and Shaping Texts	Write instructions on jobs for a robot to do.	En3/1a-e;2a-e; 5a,b;9a
	Make up poems with a rhythm about robots-machines working	En3/1a-e;2a-e; 5a,b;9a
	Write letters to a robot factory.	En3/1a-e;2a-e; 5a,b;9a
	Write a newspaper report.	En3/1a-e;2a-e; 5a,b;9a
	Write about the day there was no electricity from different people's viewpoints.	En3/1a-e;2a-f; ICT PoS 1a,b;2a,b; QCA ICT Unit 4A
Mathematics (Page 70)		
Using and Applying Mathematics	Devise electrical games that could include number, shape and measures.	Ma2/2b-j;3a
Handling Data	Collect and analyse data about the number of particular electrical devices, such as computers or TVs at home.	Ma4/2a-c; ICT PoS 1a,b;3a,b;5a; QCA ICT Unit 4D
	Organise and present data to produce graphs, tables and charts about electrical circuits and devices in the home.	Ma4/2a-c; ICT PoS 1a,b;3a,b;5a; QCA ICT Unit 4D

Circuits and Conductors

Learning Objectives	Curriculum References
Design & Technology (Page 72)	
Make electrical models and games (link with Mathematics)	PoS 1a-d;2a-e;3a-c;4a-d;5b,c; QCA DT Unit 4E
Make an alarm with a pressure switch that sounds when it is pressed down.	PoS 1a-d;2a-e;3a-c;4a-d,5b,c; QCA DT Unit 4D
Take a torch apart to find out how it works and design one.	PoS 1a-d;2a-e;3a-c;4a-d;5b,c; QCA DT Unit 4C
Design a suit for a person who works near electricity.	PoS 1a-d;2a-c;3a,b;4a,b,d;5a-c
PSHCE (Page 72)	
Identify the uses and dangers of electricity.	PoS 1a;2b;3e-g;5d-e
Know rules about electricity and why they are important.	PoS 1a-c;2a,b,c,g;3f;4a,d; 5a-c, e, g-h; QCA Citizenship Unit 8
Geography (Page 72)	
Know where electricity comes from and how it gets to our homes.	PoS 1a;4a,b;6a
Look at scales and symbols on maps.	PoS 2a,c,d; QCA Geography Unit 25
Use scales to find distances between points on different maps	PoS 2a,c,d; QCA Geography Unit 25
Compare electricity uses and sources in a different country.	PoS 1a-e;2a-g;3a-g;4a,b;5a,b; QCA Geography Unit 10
Compare resources we take for granted with a village in another country.	PoS 1a-e;2a-g;3a-g;4a,b;5a,b; QCA Geography Unit 10
Art (Page 74)	
Paint pictures of a lightning strike.	PoS 1a-c;2b,c;3a,b;5a-c
Make a collage of a silver man based on *The iron man* by Ted Hughes.	PoS 1a-c;2a-c;3a,b;5a-c
History (Page 74)	
Find out about life in Tudor times before electricity was discovered.	PoS 4a,b;5a-c; QCA History Unit 8
Compare the toys of a Tudor child and a modern child.	PoS 1a,b;2c;4a,b;11a,b; QCA History Unit 8
Research the links with electricity of Edison, Davy, Baird or Marconi.	PoS 4a,b
PE (Page 74)	
Group work: devise a group machine with different movements and sounds.	PoS 2a-c;3a,b;6a,b; QCA PE Unit 9
Devise throwing and striking games, such as those played outdoors in the past, that do not use electricity.	PoS 1a,b;7a-c
Make up a game to play without electricity indoors and write the rules.	PoS 1a,b;7a-c
Music (Page 74)	
Make up thunder and lightning music.	PoS 1b,c;2a,b;3a-c;4b,c;5c
Devise a musical round for an electric circuit.	PoS 1b,c;2a,b;3a,c;4c;5c; QCA Music Unit 11

Circuits and Conductors

The Circus Comes to Town.

The aluminium acrobats

Aluminium is a metal. How many other metals can you name?

Circ- as a prefix means circle.

Circus Circuit

Do the acrobats conduct electricity?

Use the equipment to find out.

Starting Points

- Always start with a discussion about safety when using electricity. Show and name the components to be used in each task. Emphasise that 1.5V batteries are safe but children must never try any of these investigations with mains electricity. Introduce the term 'circuit'. Simple circuits will have been taught in earlier years but need to be revised.

- Challenge groups to make a bulb light up with only wires, a 1.5V battery and a bulb. Introduce holders next to make it easier to put the circuit together.

- Discuss what happens if there is a break in the circuit. Ask the children what they think the wires are made of. They may think that they are plastic because they can only see the outside. Confirm that there is wire inside.

- Introduce the vocabulary of 'conductor' and 'insulator' and the names of devices used.

Enquiry

- Ask the children to find out which materials conduct electricity. Provide a variety of materials such as wood, paper, rubber and plastic and a variety of metals for groups to investigate. Set up a circuit with a battery, a bulb and a gap. Ask the children to predict then record what happens when each material is put in the gap. Use the activity sheet on page 67. Sort materials into good conductors and poor conductors. Explain that poor conductors that do not let electricity through the gap are called 'insulators'.

Extension Activities

- Look at different switches and decide how they work to switch a circuit on and off.

- Make up conductor models and test them to see if they work. For example, children could create foil figures. The wire ends of an open circuit can be touched one to each hand of the figure to see if the bulb will light up (see the display above). Figures of other materials could be made for experimentation.

- Look at a variety of batteries of different shapes and sizes. Note that it is the voltage and not the size of the battery that indicates how powerful it is. Note also that each has a positive and negative end.

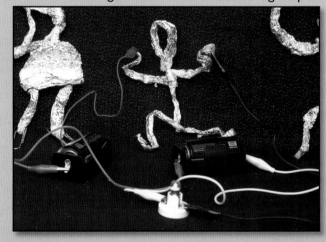

- Closely observe the inside of a large, clear bulb. Note where electricity enters and leaves it and how it travels through a metal conductor. More able children may understand why it lights up – the metal has a lot of resistance to the flow of electricity and so friction produces heat and light.

Conductors of electricity

Which of these materials conduct electricity? Predict before you test.

Name of material	Prediction (Yes or No)	Test result (Yes or No)

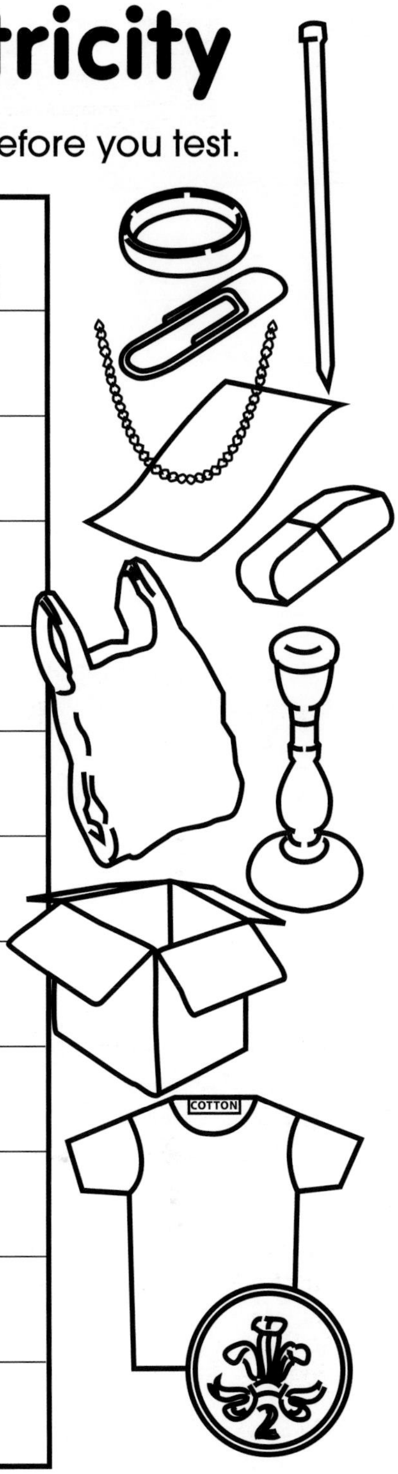

Draw a diagram to show how you tested the materials.

NOW!

Which materials are good conductors?

_____ _____ _____

_____ _____ _____

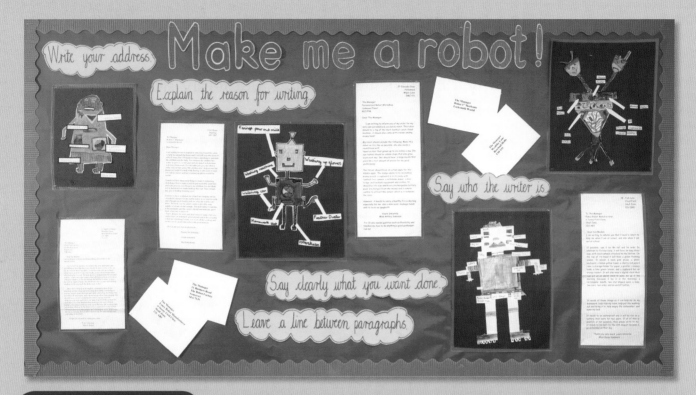

Literacy

Reading and Writing

- Ask the children to invent a robot that uses batteries. It could be useful in school or at home to do homework, make their bed, be a friend, read stories at bedtime and so on. Draw or paint what it would look like and describe what it does and how. Then compose a letter to a factory to make the robot, giving precise instructions about size, appearance and any other facts (encourage the use of the senses: what it should feel like, smell like, what its voice sounds like). Write instructions for jobs for the robot to do (see the display above).

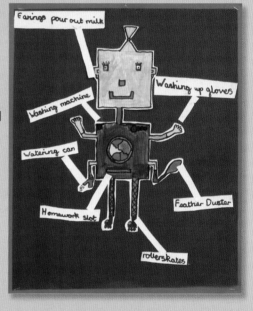

- Make up poems with a rhythm about robots or machines working. They could clap hands to the rhythm and make up words to go along with it.

- Read *The iron man* by Ted Hughes (Faber Children's Books). Discuss the descriptive writing style used by the author.

- Write about the iron man in a newspaper report.

- Start a story about the day there was no electricity. Ask the children to imagine they are different people in the town such as a shopkeeper, a bank manager, a mother, a doctor and so on and explain how it affects them. Let the children select who they want to be. Use the activity sheet on page 69 as a starting point.

- Find out about metals and where they come from. Draw a flow chart to show the production of a can of drink, from finding the ore through to the factory and on to their lunch box.

Speaking and Listening

- The children could pretend they have seen the iron man and tell a friend about the moment they saw him and how they felt or they could imagine being the iron man and tell a friend how they feel.

- Make up a silver man and describe an introduction to a story about him. Link this to Art (see page 74).

- Visit a junkyard or ask the children to think about the objects and machines in a junkyard and describe them imaginatively. Make up a class poem with the children using these ideas and asking them to imagine the junk objects coming to life. Use the senses to describe their look, smell, sound, and how they feel to the touch.

Ernie's house

At home Ernie has many things that work using electricity. How many can you think of in one minute?

One day, there is a power cut! Ernie has problems because there is no electricity at all! How can you help him?

Oh dear! I have no electricity!

For each box, think of as many solutions as you can. For instance, he might not be able to get a takeaway if there is a power cut in the whole town.

In the last two boxes think of more problems . . . and some solutions.

Problem	Solution
What can Ernie have for dinner?	He could get a takeaway meal.
How can he see to do things at night time?	
How can he save all the food in the freezer?	
What can he do instead of watching TV or playing on the computer?	
What will he do with all the dirty washing?	
How can he make a cup of tea?	

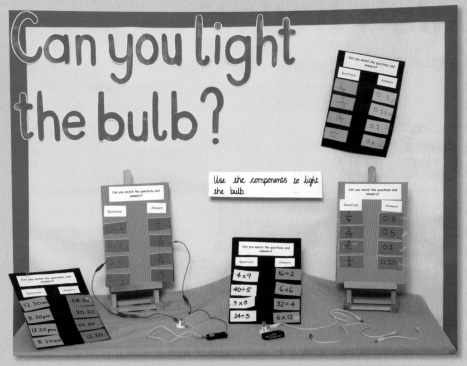

Can you light the bulb?

Use the components to light the bulb.

Using and Applying

- Make up matching questions to go with the electrical game boards on the Activity Sheet 'Fun and games' on page 71. Match equivalent fractions; decimal and vulgar fractions; multiplication and division; addition and subtraction equations and so on (see the display).

- Find out the cost of an electricity bill for a given time at home or at school and suggest ways to save money. Think of ways to remind people to switch off appliances and lights and keep a record of how well it works.

- Look at and compare different electric light bulbs including energy-saving ones. Look for the wattage (power) of each and discuss the advantages and disadvantages of using different wattages.

Handling Data

- Write a questionnaire about the different electrical devices in the home, such as the number of computers, TVs and so on. Ask the children to organise the information on a database and make graphs of some of the information,

- Use different types of information to teach children whether it is possible to draw a graph or not.
  - Compare the brightness of light bulbs with different numbers of bulbs in the circuit and record results on a table. Use two 1.5V batteries for this to get a range of results. The number of bulbs (independent factor) is a number. Judging the brightness of a bulb by looking (dependent factor that is not measurable) is recorded in words. So no graph is possible (see Table 1 below).
  - Make a table of how many children have a computer (or different electrical appliance) in their houses. The number of children (dependent factor) and of computers (or other appliances) (independent factor) are in numbers. This can convert to a bar graph. See Table 2.
  - Try other examples of the above. Provide a table of information for children to decide if they can use the information to draw a graph or not. The following are some suggestions for tables.

Number of bulbs in the circuit	Brightness of bulb
1	Bright
2	Not so bright
3	Dim

Table 1

No graph is possible as the second column has no numbers.

Number of computers in the house	Number of houses
0	5
1	15
2	4

Table 2

A bar graph can be made as the second column has numbers.

Number of motors in the circuit	How fast they go
1	Fast
2	Very slowly
3	Do not move

Table 3

No graph is possible as the second column has no numbers.

Fun and games

Amaze your friends with your home-made electricity game.

You will need:

- An A4 piece of thick, stiff cardboard
- 8 bare silver paperclips
- 4 wires with a crocodile clip on each end
- A circuit with a battery, bulb and a gap between two wires

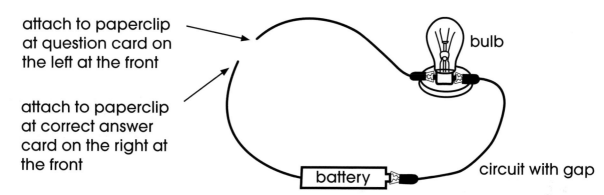

attach to paperclip at question card on the left at the front

attach to paperclip at correct answer card on the right at the front

bulb

battery

circuit with gap

Make your game up so it looks like this:

Back of board

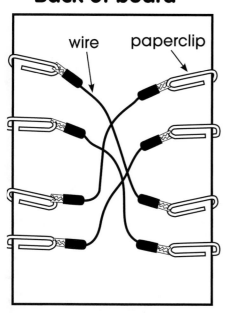

wire   paperclip

Front of board

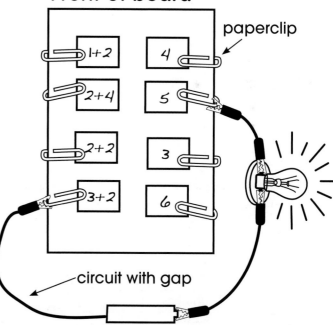

paperclip

1+2   4

2+4   5

2+2   3

3+2   6

circuit with gap

Make up some question cards and the answers and put them down each side of the board. Use your circuit with a gap by touching one free clip to a question and one to the answer. If you are correct you will make a complete circuit and the bulb will light up.

Make up some other cards about different things. You can change the wires at the back if you like. Always make sure the answers are in the right place.

Design & Technology

● Take a torch apart to find out how it works. Ask groups to put together a similar circuit and use the circuit in a model of a torch. Children should first have experience of a variety of switches to do this.

● Design a suit of a coat and trousers for a person who works in a power station near electricity. Ensure it is not made of materials that conduct electricity. They could also consider appropriate colours and design a logo for the electricity company. See the activity sheet on page 73.

● Make a burglar alarm with a pressure switch as shown below. The alarm will sound when the children press down on the card.

Folded card OPEN (from above)

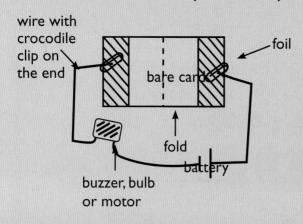

Folded card pressed to CLOSE (side view)

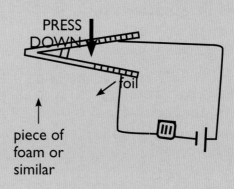

PSHCE

● Ask the children to find out about the dangers of electricity, then to design and display stickers or posters as a warning for one or more aspects of it (see the display).

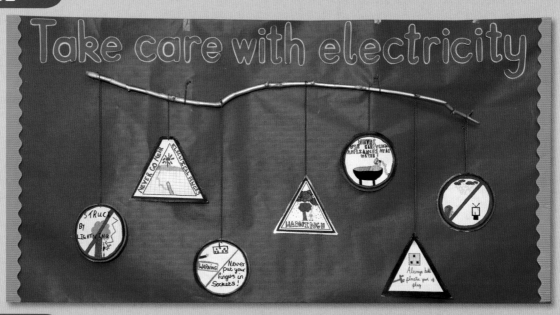

Geography

● Locate the nearest power station in the area and pinpoint it and the school on a local map. Look at scales on the map and calculate the distance electricity travels. Ask children to find out how it gets from the power station to the school.

● List the things that we take for granted everyday for which we need electricity such as leisure activities, keeping food fresh, transport, the running of school, money and so on. Compare these with a village or town in a contrasting country such as India that does not have easy access to electricity. Find out what the people in the village do for all those things we take for granted.

Circuits and Conductors

Be designers!

The new power station at Sparks' Farm
will open in July next year.

Companies are invited to present designs for the following:

a suit of a coat and trousers for workers
and
a logo for the Zig-Zag Power Station.

Presentations of the new designs will be held on
9th September at 8.00 pm
in the Meeting Room at the Zig-Zag Power Station
when the best design will be selected.

Here are basic shapes for the clothes. Cut out a suit like this, only bigger.
Use it for your presentation of ideas.

❁ In your group,
   work together as a
   company.

❁ Decide on a design.
   Think about the
   safety, colours
   and comfort of
   the materials and
   fastenings.

❁ Try out different ideas for the electricity
   company's logo and choose the best one.
   Simple ideas are often the best.

❁ Decide how to present the designs. Use the enlarged cut-out suit to
   show how your design will look.

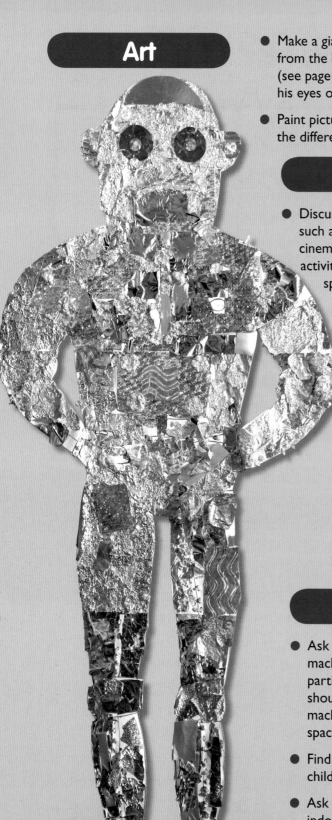

Art

- Make a giant collage of a silver man (see left) based on the iron man from the book and linked to the creative writing about a silver man (see page 68). The children could decide to make a special feature of his eyes or ears or hands and light them up using a simple circuit.

- Paint pictures of a lightning strike. Look at pictures and posters to see the different forms of lightning and how it lights up the surroundings.

History

- Discuss and compare today's leisure activities that use electricity such as television, computer games, music players, visiting the cinema, ten pin bowling alleys and so on with the type of leisure activities enjoyed in Tudor times including games, fairs, jousting, sports and so on when electricity had not been discovered.

- Use the activity sheet on page 75 for children to identify Tudor and modern day toys. Hold a Tudor day in which children can only eat food, play games and use objects that were about in Tudor times. Groups could research different aspects to share with the class and plan drama and present information about Tudor times to other classes or parents.

- Use books, the Internet and other sources to gather information about people who found out about electricity in the past such as Thomas Edison (1847–1931), Humphrey Davy (1778–1829), John Logie Baird (1888–1946) who was the inventor of TV, Guglielmo Marconi (1874–1937) and others. Make cartoon strips to show what they did or make up a group display to show others about their work.

PE

- Ask groups to plan the movement and sound of an electrical machine. Each part needs to have a repetitive movement and a particular sound and work together with other parts. Groups should decide what the machine does and the place where the machine is switched on and off. Encourage the use of direction, space, flexibility and all parts of the body.

- Find out about and play striking and throwing games that children played in the past, that do not use electricity.

- Ask groups or pairs of children to make up a game to play indoors that does not use electricity and to write the rules. The simplest are often the best!

Music

- Discuss how to make the sounds of lightning and which instruments will make the best sounds for this. Make lightning sounds, add the sounds of thunder and rain to build up a storm that gradually dies out and finishes. Together, write the music for it. Elect a conductor to show which instrument should play, when and how loudly and quickly.

- Devise a 'round and round' round for an electric circuit.

Then and now

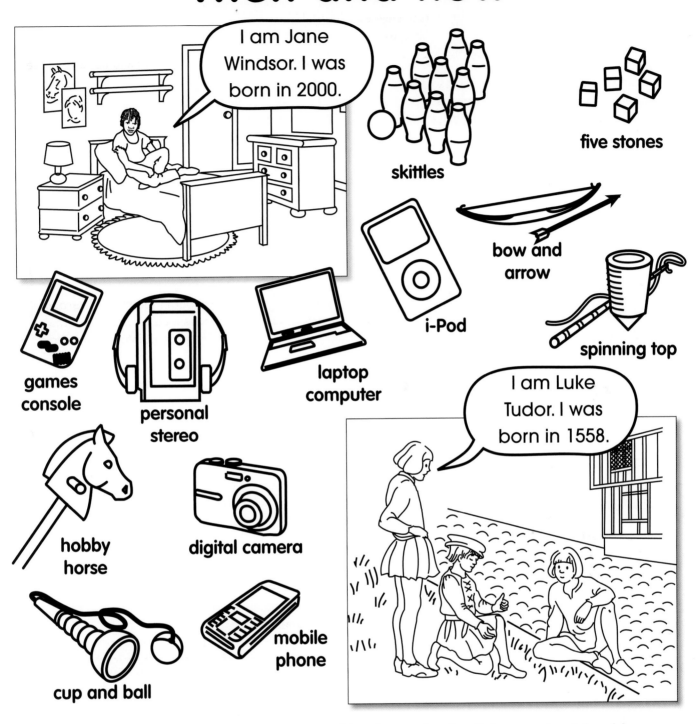

skittles

five stones

I am Jane Windsor. I was born in 2000.

bow and arrow

i-Pod

spinning top

games console

personal stereo

laptop computer

I am Luke Tudor. I was born in 1558.

hobby horse

digital camera

cup and ball

mobile phone

Jane lives in the twenty-first century. She has plastic things, electrical toys and lots of toys and games.

Luke lived in the sixteenth century. There was no plastic, no electricity and there were not many toys or games.

Draw a line from each toy or game to either Jane or Luke to show which they would have.

NOW!

Which electrical toy do you think Luke would have liked most if it had been available in the sixteenth century?

Find out about one of Luke's games or toys.

Assessment Ideas

In any activity the children carry out, whether through discussing, planning, doing or writing, there is an element of assessment. There are many ways to assess children, see the ideas below and the grid on page 77 for further suggestions. Knowledge-based assessments should use a variety of methods such as games, quizzes, drama and role play presentations, discussion of 'concept cartoons' and completing 'concept maps'.

● Concept cartoons are a useful tool in teaching and assessing. Each cartoon takes an everyday scientific idea about which three or more points of view are shown. For example, it could be a variety of views about how quickly objects fall. The cartoons encourage children to think carefully about what is being discussed and say which point of iew they agree with and why. The cartoons generally portray a range of ideas which can be used to promote discussion of the children's own ideas and inform teachers what to teach and how to group children. For more information visit www.conceptcartoons.com

● Concept maps are also useful. The idea is to link nouns about a theme with arrows. The arrow shows the connection between the two words. For example:

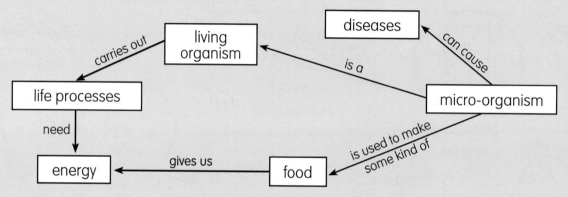

● Ensure that you have clear learning objectives for your lessons and that these are shared and understood by the children.

● Tell the children what the success criteria are and how they can achieve them.

● When marking children's work, highlight successes against the learning objective and write affirmative statements on the page such as 'you can make a circuit' or 'you can name parts of the body'.

● Include time for assessment work in your daily and weekly planning. You may wish to conduct an end of topic investigation to access the children's level of knowledge and understanding.

● At the end of the topic, create a spreadsheet document to record the children's attainment against the objectives. Colour-code the cells: red for not achieved, orange for objective met and green for those who have exceeded expectations. This will produce an 'at a glance' reference to achievement and will highlight areas that need further work. Such documents could be handed on with other record-keeping to inform planning in subsequent year groups.

● Self-assessment sheets for children to complete are included on pages 78–80. The sheets cover areas of knowledge taught throughout the year. Children should be given their own sheets at the end of teaching a theme for them to colour in the objectives achieved. These could be colour-coded for those areas they think they know well/are uncertain about/do not know. The 'I can ...' statements of skills will be practised in different contexts throughout the year, so children need to make judgements on each one more than once, again at the end of each theme and they should write the date in the column when the skill is achieved. Use all the sheets alongside your assessments to inform reports and general assessment at the end of the school year.

Who Should Assess?

● Anyone involved with children's learning can assess, including parents and the children themselves. The most important thing is that the assessor knows what they are looking for and has the skills and knowledge to make these judgements. Children can assess each other – but they should always try to be constructive – what are the good points as well as the not so good?

HOW	TIPS
Observation of Children Working	Use this method when there is no written work as evidence, for example, when children are planning and discussing. Assess a single child or a group by questioning the children to clarify understanding.
Group Feedback	Use this method to clarify the understanding of 'quiet' children or those you are unsure about. Allow the 'listening' children to ask questions of 'presenters'. Ask questions of the children to gain a greater understanding of their learning.
Recording Children's Views During an Activity	Gather the children's opinions and ideas during activities. Ask the children to make their own recordings for you to listen to after the lesson.
Drama	This method is fun and non-threatening for children as they can 'show' instead of write their understanding of key objectives. Use role play to discuss issues and act out events and imaginary situations such as, 'inside a part of the body', 'in space' or 'inside the Earth' to clarify understanding of key concepts.
Concept Cartoons	Use at the beginning and/or at the end of lessons to clarify children's ideas.
Diagrams, Drawings and Photographs	Ask the children to draw ideas before teaching and at the end to compare understanding of concepts. Make or interpret concept maps before and after lessonsor topics. Photograph the children's work before and after the topic is complete to compare.
Sort a Collection	Ask the children to sort a collection of objects/vocabulary related to the topic in different ways. This method is particularly good for Maths and Science, to pinpoint the children's grasp of skills and knowledge.
Make & Play a Game	Incorporate key concepts and vocabulary into games, for example, create questions that the children have to answer correctly before they move a space on a board game. Laminate games and retain for future use.
Devise & Answer Questions	Put questions in a box (generated by the teacher and the children) and ask the children to answer them over the course of the topic.
Interactive Display	Put questions on displays which highlight key concepts instead of labels. Add to the display as the topic progresses.
Types of Quiz	Create a true/false quiz on areas of knowledge and play this before and after teaching the topic to compare the children's responses. Quizzes can be oral or written by children or teacher.
Written Work	Writing is useful as evidence but be aware that this is not always the best way for children to demonstrate what they know or can do. Use different genres of writing.

Life Processes and Living Things

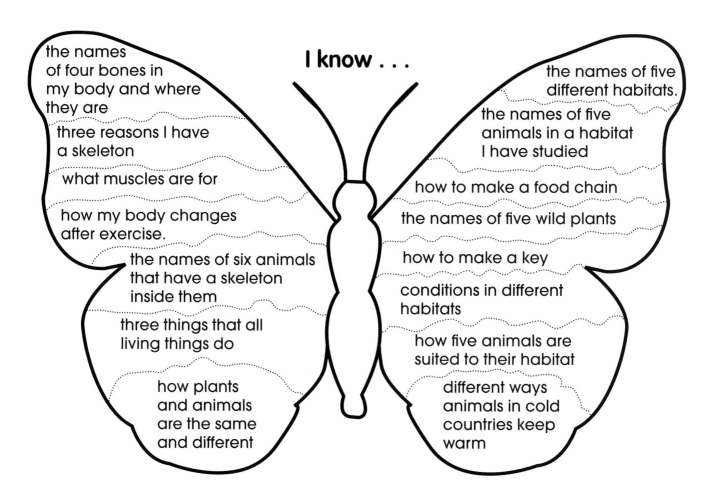

I know . . .

the names of four bones in my body and where they are

three reasons I have a skeleton

what muscles are for

how my body changes after exercise.

the names of six animals that have a skeleton inside them

three things that all living things do

how plants and animals are the same and different

the names of five different habitats.

the names of five animals in a habitat I have studied

how to make a food chain

the names of five wild plants

how to make a key

conditions in different habitats

how five animals are suited to their habitat

different ways animals in cold countries keep warm

Scientific Enquiry

I can...

Skill	Date	Date	Date	Skill	Date	Date	Date
tell about the work of a scientist				share ideas with others			
ask questions about things around me				plan what to do to answer questions			
suggest ways of answering questions				decide on the equipment I will need			
use scientific language to describe and explain things				predict what will happen			
suggest different ways to find information				give a reason for a prediction			

Materials and their Properties

I know…

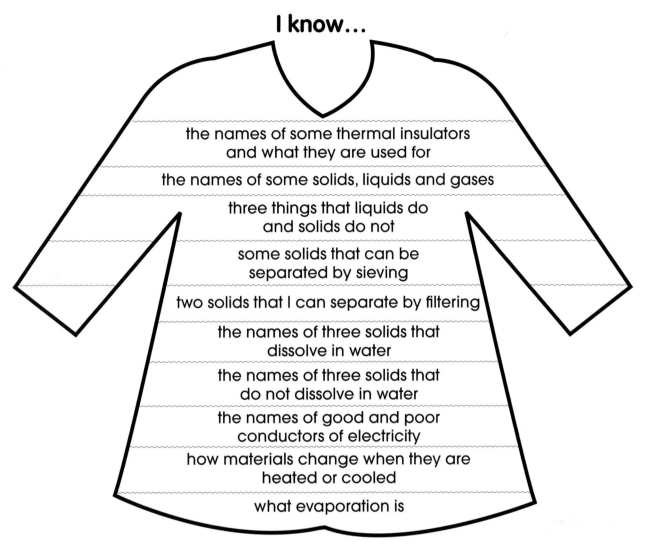

the names of some thermal insulators and what they are used for

the names of some solids, liquids and gases

three things that liquids do and solids do not

some solids that can be separated by sieving

two solids that I can separate by filtering

the names of three solids that dissolve in water

the names of three solids that do not dissolve in water

the names of good and poor conductors of electricity

how materials change when they are heated or cooled

what evaporation is

Scientific Enquiry

I can…

Skill	Date	Date	Date	Skill	Date	Date	Date
carry out an enquiry with help				draw and label a table without help			
carry out an enquiry without help				use a computer to collect and store information			
work with others				use different measuring equipment			
decide how to record my work				observe carefully			
say if a test is fair or not				decide whether a graph can be drawn from results or not			
draw a table with help				make a bar chart from results			

Physical Processes

I know…

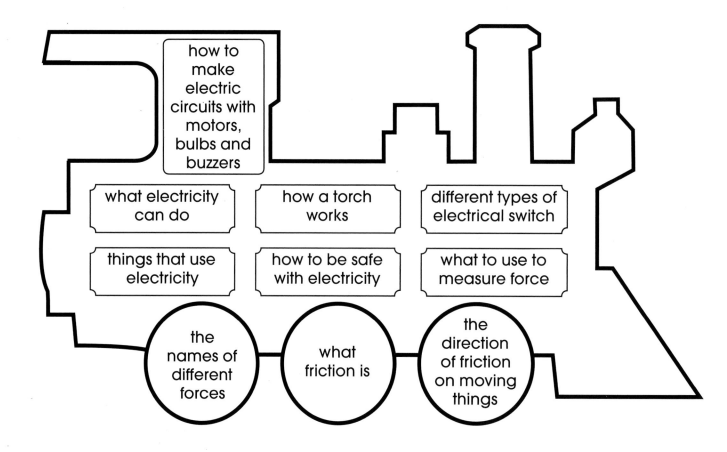

how to make electric circuits with motors, bulbs and buzzers

what electricity can do

how a torch works

different types of electrical switch

things that use electricity

how to be safe with electricity

what to use to measure force

the names of different forces

what friction is

the direction of friction on moving things

Scientific Enquiry

I can…

Skill	Date	Date	Date	Skill	Date	Date	Date
describe what happens in an enquiry				compare results with my prediction			
use results to compare things				say how I could improve my enquiry			
find a pattern in my results				present results to other people			